Young Readers Nature Library

THE UNIVERSE

Young Readers Nature Library
Adapted from the LIFE Nature Library

THE UNIVERSE

David Bergamini
and the Editors of TIME-LIFE BOOKS

TIME-LIFE BOOKS, ALEXANDRIA, VIRGINIA

ON THE COVER: The Andromeda galaxy
burns with fierce beauty some two million
light-years out in space. Though lying near
the Milky Way, the Andromeda galaxy
is not a part of it. One of the two satellite
galaxies of Andromeda is seen to the
left of the white hub of the main galaxy.

Contents

HEAVENLY SYMBOLS marking the constellations
are labeled with their Latin names in this 17th
Century engraving. The figures on the straight line
along which the sun moves *(center)* are in the section
of sky called the zodiac. Known as the signs of the
zodiac, the symbols are still used by astrologers.

1

The Early Explorers
of the Heavens

We of the latter part of the 20th Century are living in a time of man's greatest adventure: his first flights away from the earth toward the unmeasured expanses of the universe. Men have climbed the mountains of the moon, penetrated the mists of Venus and landed an unmanned spacecraft on Mars. Within centuries, whole colonies of people may embark on voyages that will last for generations.

This age of human daring and resourcefulness is dawning just as our knowledge of the entire universe, or cosmos, is more humbling than ever before. We once thought with confidence that the universe—moon, sun, planets and stars—revolved around us. Now we know that the earth is one smallish planet of a medium-sized star in the outskirts of only one of billions of galaxies.

From earliest times, man has gazed into the night sky and pondered the glittering patterns he saw there. Before writing was invented, man had names for the celestial bodies. To nomad and seafarer, the stars in the sky were signposts that told direction. To farmer and herdsman, the moon's phases and the sun's annual journey foretold the times of planting and of rains. The motions of celestial bodies were recorded for such purely practical reasons long before astronomy earned the name of a science.

In all early civilizations, what we call astronomy went hand in glove with astrology, fortunetelling and superstition. In ancient Mesopotamia, for instance, priests mapped the yearly path—called the ecliptic—of the sun across the heavens, and could predict eclipses of the moon. But, mixing their knowledge with awesome rituals, they kept it a mystery to simple men.

The first truly scientific astronomers were Greek. The Greeks had an invaluable scientific asset, geometry, which they developed, with astronomy, into a marvelous intellectual instrument. The first school of Greek astronomy—and the most imaginative of them—grew up not in Greece itself but in Greek colonies south of Troy along the present Turkish coast. As early as 600 B.C., the philosopher Thales conceived of the earth as a round, flat disk. Two centuries later, the disciples of Pythagoras believed that the earth was spherical and that it also moved through space. Still later when Aristarchus of Samos (310-230 B.C.) maintained that the earth rotated on its axis, revolved around the sun and was *not* the center of the cosmos, he was publicly reprimanded for disrespect of the gods. To most people his ideas seemed both ridiculous and antireligious.

Conservative stargazers gradually adopted a more consistent, although more complicated, representation of the motions they saw in the sky. Their theory was finally formulated by one of the most careful and scientific of all Greek astronomers, Hipparchus, about 150 B.C. According to Hipparchus' observations and calculations, the spherical earth was stationary; the sun, moon and planets circled the earth in a major sweep; and at the same time, they followed other circular courses centered on the first orbits.

Hipparchus' complicated geometry accurately represented the motions that the early astronomers observed and also made predictions possible. His system was perfected about 140 A.D. by Claudius Ptolemy, a

PTOLEMY'S
SYSTEM

When Ptolemy Was King

Until the 16th Century, scientists and laymen alike thought the earth was the center of the universe. This view was perfected in Egypt in the Second Century A.D. by the Greek astronomer Ptolemy, who believed that the sun, moon and planets moved around the stationary earth in complex orbits. His system, represented above in a 17th Century Dutch illustration, plots the orbits of the moon, Mercury, Venus, the sun, Mars, Jupiter and Saturn. Ptolemy himself is shown at left in a drawing from an early 16th Century book. He is enthroned as the king of astronomers, holding a star-gauging instrument in one hand and supporting a globe of the universe.

9

THE
COPERNICAN
SYSTEM

Putting the Sun in the Center

After 1,300 years of popular acceptance, the theory of an earth-centered universe began to be destroyed. The man largely responsible for demolishing the misconception was a brilliant Polish lawyer-astronomer named Nicholas Copernicus (*left*), who in 1543 said it was the sun, not the earth, that was the center of our system. This 17th Century drawing shows him holding a symbol of the earth circling the sun. The Copernican system was oversimplified, as can be seen above; Copernicus thought the planets orbited the sun in perfect circles. But the fact that he put the sun at the center in time revolutionized astronomy.

Greek who lived in Alexandria. It was recorded in the form of an astronomical encyclopedia, Ptolemy's famous *Almagest*. This system was so good that it withstood the tests of observation for another 13 centuries. Because of Ptolemy's great work, Hipparchus' scheme became known as the Ptolemaic system.

Great technical difficulties helped the Ptolemaic system to go unchallenged. The two largest of these difficulties were time and numbers. Time was a problem because there was no really precise way of measuring it. What use, after all, were accurate fixes on planet positions at midnight if no one really knew that it *was* midnight? Numbers were a problem because the ancients had no good way of expressing them. In the system of numbers used by the Romans and the Alexandrian Greeks it seemed almost impossible to express the smallest astronomic quantities. In Roman numerals, for instance, the mileage to the moon would be written CCXXXMMMMMMMMDCCCLVII instead of 238,857. To us this might seem just a matter of clumsy notation, but to the ancients it was a major mental block. Only Archimedes, one of the last of the great Greek scientists (287-212 B.C.), was ever completely at home with big numbers. But his mind was exceptional: he worked out most of the mathematical laws governing levers, pulleys, gears and hydraulics—that is, much of everyday mechanics. When Rome attacked Syracuse, he held the enemy

fleet at bay for three years with engines of war that hurled huge boulders at the Roman ships or lifted them bodily out of the water to smash them against the Sicilian cliffs.

Where big numbers were concerned, Archimedes saw such difficulty that he devoted a whole treatise to the subject, which he entitled *The Sand Reckoner*. "There are some," he wrote, "who think that the number of the sand is infinite in multitude . . . But I will try to show . . . that, of the numbers named by me . . . some exceed the number of a mass of sand equal in magnitude to the universe." The largest unit that the Greeks used was a "myriad"—10,000. Archimedes showed, by a series of calculations with cumbersome numerals, that what he thought of as the universe could not hold as much as the following number of sand grains: a myriad of myriads multiplied by itself seven times and then multiplied by a thousand myriads. Today, mathematicians represent this huge number as the numeral 1 followed by 63 zeros (or as 10^{63}).

Numbers like 10^{63} are still big enough to deal with the universe we know today. The world's largest telescope, for instance, sees out to the edge of a volume of about 10^{68} cubic miles (1 followed by 68 zeros). The number of electrons that could be packed into a sphere as big as the earth is about 10^{63}. In visualizing either very big or very small things, modern man deals with Archimedean-sized numbers. And though we can now express them easily, it is still difficult for us to appreciate their actual size.

During the Middle Ages the main advances of importance to astronomy were the development of clocks and European adoption of the Arabic numerals and system of numbers we use today. Actually, this system was not perfected in Arabia at all, but in India. There, about 500 A.D., the Hindus started using a 10-number (decimal) notation in which the position of each digit showed its value, increasing ten times in each place from right to left, while the empty positions were filled by zeros. From India the new system spread west to the Muslim world until it finally reached the capitals of Christendom about 1100 A.D.

Along with more easily handled numbers, the Christian world got from the Arabs its first translations of the astronomical works of pre-Ptolemaic Greeks. Some important instruments, too, were copied from the Muslims, but the all-important clock seems to have had its main development in Europe. The first mechanical clocks appeared toward the end of the 13th Century. They were run not by springs but by descending weights that hung from strings, and they were not very accurate. Even in 1450 A.D., the best of the pre-Copernican Italian astronomers, Toscanelli, was seldom able to give anything more exact about his observations than the nearest hour and the date.

By 1500 A.D., the improved quality of astronomical observation was beginning to strain the ancient Ptolemaic theory with a mass of new facts. The man who threw the final bomb into the celestial machinery was the Polish astronomer Copernicus (1473-1543). He dethroned the earth and put the sun at the center of all the orbiting planets. But he still showed the planets' orbits as circles, not the ellipses they really are.

Martin Luther called Copernicus a fool and his theories anti-Biblical and intolerable. The Pope (Paul III) was inclined to be more tolerant, but many bishops and cardinals agreed with Luther. Some fellow-scientists rallied to Copernicus' defense. One of them was burned at the stake, and others saw their careers ruined and their names smeared with the charge of heresy. Copernicanism became such a thorny religious issue that the best astronomical observer of the 16th Century, Tycho Brahe, would have no part of it. But the data Tycho compiled at his elaborate observatories in Denmark—the most accurate ever assembled up to that time—only helped others to prove the Copernican system right.

When Galileo first turned a telescope on the skies, in 1609, he found the Copernican system staring him in the face. Around the planet Jupiter he saw four moons circling: clear proof that earth, with only one moon, could not be the most important member of celestial society. Galileo also observed the moonlike phases of Venus. The fact that Venus showed a fully lighted phase when it was near the sun could not be explained by the Ptolemaic system, but only

Proof from a Mistaken Master

One of the astronomers who did not accept the Copernican idea that the planets orbited the sun was the Dane Tycho Brahe *(below)*, who still thought the earth was the center of the system. In the late 1500s he designed the best astronomical instruments yet known. With them he plotted the positions of 1,000 stars on a five-foot globe of the heavens, seen at the right with an umbrellalike dust cover. His accurate records helped later scientists to prove that Copernicus, not Brahe, was right.

TYCHO'S GLOBE OF THE HEAVENS

ENGLISH ASTRONOMICAL WATCH

GERMAN BOOK-SHAPED WATCH

GERMAN ASTRONOMICAL CALENDAR CLOCK

GERMAN SUNDIAL WITH COMPASS

by a Copernican scheme that would allow Venus to circle around the far side of the sun. Because of these observations, Galileo became such an ardent Copernican that the Inquisition forced him to make a public denial of his astronomical theories, and placed him under permanent house arrest. He was forbidden to raise the matter again, and spent the rest of his days in the study of mechanics and dynamics.

By the next generation, however, religious opposition to a sun-centered universe was dying out. In the Protestant north, the suc-cessor to Tycho Brahe was Johannes Kepler (1571-1630). Using Tycho's observations, he showed that a planet does not travel in that exactly circular orbit so vital to the Greek ideal of perfection, but instead fol-lowed a slightly elliptical course. This is the first of Kepler's three laws—the three essential laws of the solar system that he had the luck and wit to discover singlehand-edly. The second law is that the planets, in their elliptical orbits, move faster when close to the sun than they do when farther away. The third law is that there is a def-

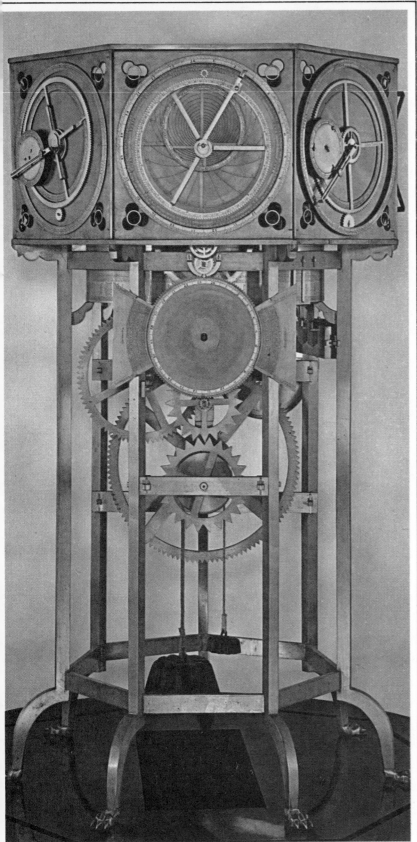

DE DONDI'S MECHANICAL CLOCK

AUSTRIAN GLOBE OF THE HEAVENS

The Rise of Clocks

Astronomers need highly accurate clocks to record the positions and movements of stars and planets. No reliable clocks were made until 1362, when an Italian, Giovanni de Dondi, built the masterpiece shown in replica at left. This clock told time and also showed the movements of the planets. By the 16th and 17th Centuries elegant celestial globes and accurate clocks were being manufactured all over Europe (*above and far left*).

15

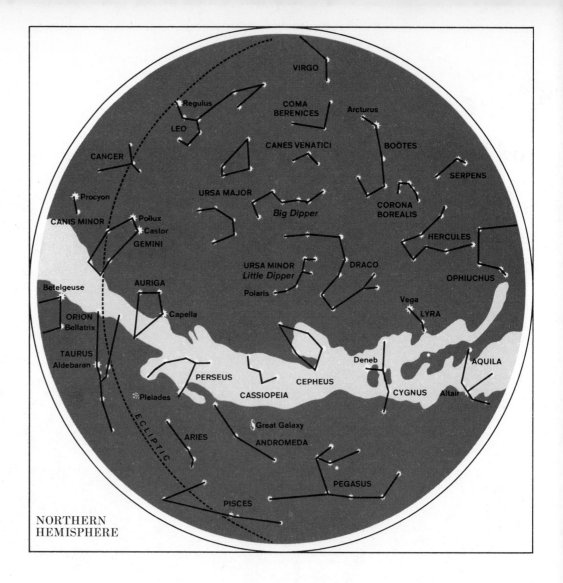

NORTHERN
HEMISPHERE

inite mathematical relation between all the planets' distances from the sun and the times they take to complete their orbits.

Isaac Newton (1642-1727) based his universal law of gravitation on Kepler's three laws, together with Galileo's pioneering work on mechanics. Newton, agreeing with Galileo, stated that a body would move in a straight line with constant speed unless a force caused it to change its motion. Since the planets moved in curved paths around the sun, there must be a force between the planets and the sun pulling the planet toward the sun. This force is gravitation. The

gravitational pull toward the sun combined with the planet's sideways motion makes the planet move in an elliptical path around the sun.

Newton saw that not only the sun and the planets, but each object in the universe exerts a gravitational force on every other object. The amount of this force depends partly on the amount of matter the objects contain (their masses). He saw that what makes ordinary objects fall to earth is the gravitational power of the earth's mass. He was able to calculate the pull between the earth and the moon and so explain why the

SOUTHERN
HEMISPHERE

moon moves as it does. He explained that the moon exerts a different amount of gravitational pull on the earth's nearer surface than on the farther surface—and that this difference causes the tides of the oceans.

Newton's ideas and equations swept the world. Neptune and Pluto, two unseen planets, were calculated to exist by Newtonian principles—and were duly discovered. The laws of light and other electromagnetic waves, of chemistry and of atomic physics all were discovered, often prompted by the desire to solve problems in astronomy. The

(Text continued on page 20)

The Constellations We See

The maps on these pages show the brightest stars and star-groups, or constellations, that can be seen in the Northern and Southern Hemispheres. The major constellations are named in capital letters; important stars are marked in small letters. One of the most familiar groups of the northern skies is the Big Dipper, which is actually part of the larger constellation Ursa Major (The Big Bear). The Little Dipper, containing Polaris, the North Star, is part of Ursa Minor (The Little Bear). The Milky Way is seen as a cloudy belt across each map.

17

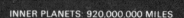

INNER PLANETS: 920,000,000 MILES

EARTH AND MOON: 920,000 MILES

EARTH: 7,927 MILES

How Big Is the Universe?

The enormous size of the known universe is
suggested by this sequence of imaginary cubes. The
earth (*left*) and its moon are shown in the first cube
(*above left*), which represents a space 920,000 miles
wide; in the next view, this cube is found inside
one that represents a space a thousand times wider
than the first cube. This process is repeated up to
the last cube at right, which contains the nearby
galaxies. To include the *farthest* galaxies we can see,
the next cube in the series would have to enclose a
space 156,000 billion billion miles wide—nearly 170
times as wide as the last one at the right!

SOLAR NEIGHBORHOOD: 920,000,000,000 MILES

NEARBY STARS: 920,000,000,000,000 MILES

MILKY WAY: 920,000,000,000,000,000 MILES

NEARBY GALAXIES: 920,000,000,000,000,000,000 MILES

Matt. Greene

sun was proved to be no more the center of the universe than the earth had been; it was moving, with all its planets around it, toward the constellation of Cygnus. The center of the sun's orbit turned out to be the hub of a huge wheel of stars called the Milky Way, sometimes referred to as "our" galaxy. Beyond the last dimensions of this system, millions of similar galaxies were discovered, so far away that light from the nearest external one began traveling toward the earth more than two million years ago.

Even before man knew of these other galaxies, or realized the enormous distances with which he had to cope, Newton's beautiful equations had begun to falter. Newly discovered facts about light and other forms of radiation destroyed the simple idea of stationary space that Newton had visualized.

In his theory of relativity, Albert Einstein (1879-1955) redefined the nature of space. By clarifying and extending Newton's other assumptions in the light of his theories, Einstein rewrote the classical mechanics of astronomy and corrected Newton's equations according to the new information.

Perhaps relativity, too, will have to be corrected eventually for increasingly large phenomena, just as it has already corrected Newtonian mechanics. But the changes made in Newton's classical picture by Einstein's relativity have been small—more in the nature of improvements than of revolutionary overthrow. Modern astronomers can confidently predict that our present picture of the universe, explained in the rest of this book, is fundamentally correct.

This does not mean that astronomy is anywhere near being completed. Today's astronomers and astronauts are like citizens of a single village who have learned the size and shape of the earth but still have not explored all its forests, deserts, peaks, shores, glaciers, caverns and ocean floors. Newton himself expressed perfectly the point of view that all his successors try to emulate. "I do not know what I may appear to the world," he wrote late in his life, "but to myself I seem to have been only like a boy playing on the seashore, and diverting myself in now and then finding a smoother pebble or a prettier shell than ordinary, whilst the great ocean of truth lay all undiscovered before me."

The Receding Galaxies

Each white ball at right represents a galaxy speeding away from our galaxy (center). They are moving so fast that their light crowds up in blue waves in front and trails red waves behind. Each inner ball shows where the galaxy was when it gave off the light we see; the outer one shows where it is now.

AN INSTRUMENT-LADEN ROOFTOP in Danzig,
Poland, served as the observatory of Johannes
Hevelius, a 17th Century amateur astronomer who
won lasting fame for his work. Hevelius plotted the
surface of the moon in detail, recorded 1,564 stars,
observed sunspots and discovered four comets.

2
Mighty Instruments to Probe the Skies

When Newton died, the future of astronomy looked straightforward and simple. Star gazers would grind larger, more powerful lenses for their telescopes and improve the precision of their instruments; with these they would determine the masses and motions of the solar system and go on to study all the stars beyond. But these optimistic ambitions were repeatedly frustrated. The great frustrater was light.

The unruly nature of light had been glimpsed even before Newton's day. Indeed, Newton conquered one of its major challenges. This was the problem of chromatic aberration, the "color error" caused by the way light spreads out into a rainbow when it passes through a prism or wedge-shaped piece of glass. The early telescopes were all

lens instruments, of the type called refractors today—essentially magnifying glasses at the ends of tubes. In the simplest refractor the main lens collects the light and bends it to a focal point, while the second lens, the eyepiece, enlarges the image. But lenses also act as prisms, bending the different colors of light—the different wave lengths—by different amounts. The short waves of blue light are bent more than the longer waves of red light. As a result, the blue light focuses sooner after passing through the lens than the red light does. Thus "white" starlight, containing light of all wave lengths or colors, is focused in separate images; neither the blue one nor the red one is sharp because out-of-focus rays from the images of other colors fuzz them up.

One way to solve this problem is to bend all wave lengths as little as possible, but this makes the focus lie very far beyond the lens. Before Newton, telescopes with long focal lengths were the only solution. In the most extreme designs, called aerial telescopes, the main lens was simply strung up on top of a pole and the astronomer sat a hundred feet or more below it with his eyepiece. Johannes Hevelius (1611-1687), who mapped the moon, used an aerial telescope 150 feet long—as tall as a 12-story building. Christiaan Huygens (1629-1695), the Dutch astronomer who was the first man to make out the form of Saturn's rings, built aerial telescopes 210 feet long.

Clumsy instruments like these were not for Newton. He overcame color error by inventing a totally new type of telescope, the reflector. In a reflecting telescope, the main light-collector is not a lens at all, but a mirror curved in the shape of a parabola. Color error is avoided because all the wave lengths of light bounce equally from the mirror and are focused into a single image by its parabolic curvature.

The workaday tools of modern astronomy are reflectors, and one of the largest is the Hale telescope—an enormous 200-inch mirror mounted in a nest of metal girders within a dome a mile above sea level on California's Palomar Mountain. Like the 40-inch Yerkes refractor and another of America's largest telescopes—the 100-inch Mount Wilson reflector—the Palomar giant was conceived by George Ellery Hale (1868-1938), one of America's greatest astronomers. Hale started work on the 200-inch model in 1928, but died before his great project was completed. Finally in 1948, with the most perfect optics and mounting of any telescope on earth, the Hale 200-inch telescope went into use. Since then, it has done more to advance astronomy than any other instrument in the course of history—except perhaps the 100-inch Mount Wilson telescope, which preceded it, or Galileo's original tiny refractor.

Each new instrument in astronomy has led to fresh observations and ideas. Tycho Brahe's improved angle-measuring devices enabled Kepler to unravel the laws of the solar system. By 1845, William Parsons, third Earl of Rosse, had built a 72-inch

How Bright Are the Stars?

Distance can have an important effect on how bright a star appears to observers on the earth. The two stars drawn at left are of different brightness, but they look equally bright to us because the fainter one is considerably closer. When two stars very far away are separated by the same distance (*right*), this distance is so small compared to the total distance from us that it is no longer important. Both stars now appear nearly as different in brightness as they really are.

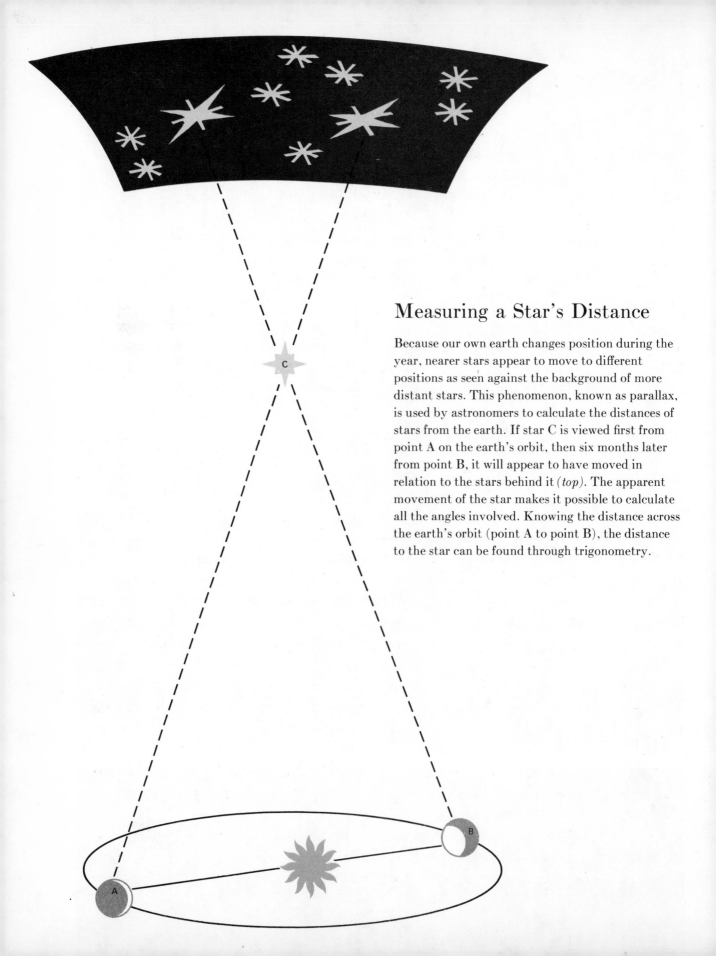

Measuring a Star's Distance

Because our own earth changes position during the year, nearer stars appear to move to different positions as seen against the background of more distant stars. This phenomenon, known as parallax, is used by astronomers to calculate the distances of stars from the earth. If star C is viewed first from point A on the earth's orbit, then six months later from point B, it will appear to have moved in relation to the stars behind it *(top)*. The apparent movement of the star makes it possible to calculate all the angles involved. Knowing the distance across the earth's orbit (point A to point B), the distance to the star can be found through trigonometry.

reflector inside a 52-foot tube on his Irish estate. With this giant telescope he discovered the structure of spiral galaxies. As for the 200-inch telescope, it has revealed billions of new stars and remote galaxies.

Over the years, big telescopes have been set up on every continent. Meanwhile, astronomers have devised such precise mountings for their instruments that telescopes now can track their targets accurately despite the daily rotation of the earth. The 200-inch Hale telescope has been trained on stars to make long-exposure photographs for as much as seven hours, and has captured pinpoint-sharp pictures.

At the foundation of all astronomical observation is light. Some of the uses of light are comparatively simple and straightforward. For example, the only direct way to measure a star's distance from the earth is by a trick of geometry known as parallax. Parallax is a measure of the amount by which an object seems to move against its background when an observer looks at it from two different places. The way parallax works can be suggested by the way something close to you—say a lamp on a table—seems to move against a picture on the wall behind it when you look at it first with one eye closed and then with the other.

As the earth moves, a nearby star seems to move in the same way against a background of distant stars. An astronomer measures the parallax of such a star by photographing it, waiting six months for the earth to move him to a point 186 million miles away on the other side of the sun, then photographing it again and measuring how the star has shifted in relation to the far-off stars. By using the convenient revolution of the earth to move their telescopes to new sighting positions, astronomers have measured the parallaxes of some 6,000 of the nearest stars.

The nearest stars are so far away that even a base line 186 million miles long is still so short that it is very difficult to measure their shift. In 1838 the German astronomer Friedrich Wilhelm Bessel first measured the parallax of 61 Cygni, one of the nearest stars. The displacement Bessel found at six-month intervals was an angle of only three tenths of a second—three tenths of a 60th of a 60th of a 360th of a full circle. Yet this tiny arc shows that 61 Cygni is 65 trillion miles away from the earth. (For simplicity's sake, astronomers call this distance 11 light-years. A light-year is the distance that light, moving at about 186,000 miles a second, travels in a year, or nearly six trillion miles. The sun is only eight light-minutes away from the earth.) Within months of Bessel's great measurement, Thomas Henderson in South Africa measured the distance to Alpha Centauri, the nearest star to the sun that can be seen with the naked eye—4.3 light-years away.

Beyond some 400 light-years the angle of parallax is too small to be measured accurately. So astronomers measure distances beyond the range of parallax by other methods. These methods depend on peculiarities of the stars themselves. The light from stars within parallactic range has revealed that some stars belong to certain clearly defined and easily recognizable classes, which always have the same real brightness no matter how much their apparent brightness is dimmed by distance. (Two 100-watt bulbs have the same *real* brightness, but if one of them is only three feet away from you its apparent brightness is much greater than that of another a hundred yards away.) When stars belonging to these special classes are found beyond the range of parallax, astronomers can estimate their distance by the decrease in their brightness. This method has served to measure cosmic distances of millions of light-years—millions of millions of millions of miles.

Classifying the stars so as to judge their distances (and their motions and masses) involved new understandings of the messages light brings from the stars. One such message was studied in 1814 by the German optician Joseph von Fraunhofer. Newton had shown that white sunlight bent by a prism forms a rainbow of all the colors. But Fraunhofer found that the sun's spectrum, as this rainbow is called, was slashed by hundreds of dark lines. Fraunhofer carefully plotted the locations of as many of these lines as he could—today they number in the thousands—but he had no idea what they meant. More than 40 years later, laboratory studies of the spectra of white-hot

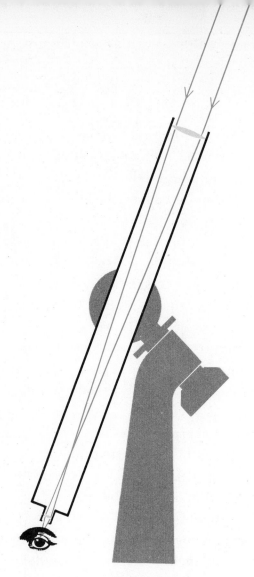

A Simple Telescope at Work

The earliest type of telescope, which Galileo *(far right)* used, is shown at right and seen in detail above. It is called a refractor telescope and works on the same principle as binoculars or microscopes. Light is gathered through a lens at the top of the long tube. The light rays are refracted, or bent, by the lens, meeting in a focus just above the eyepiece, where an image is formed. This image is magnified by a series of lenses. Galileo's telescopes were comparatively simple and could only magnify up to 20 times. But with them he began solving many of the fundamental mysteries of the universe.

GALILEO'S TELESCOPES

NEWTONIAN TELESCOPE

CASSEGRAINIAN TELESCOPE

elements showed bright slashes that perfectly matched the dark lines that Fraunhofer had so meticulously mapped.

Today, all this is explained by atomic theory. Each element—or kind of atom—can give off and absorb energy only at the specific wave lengths dictated by its atomic structure. In the spectrum of a white-hot substance each bright line is caused by atoms of an element that emit, or throw off, energy at the wave lengths prescribed for that element. In the spectrum of the sun, each dark line is caused by cooler atoms of an element in the solar atmosphere that *absorb* radiation at that particular element's set of wave lengths. The study of these mysterious absorption and emission lines in the spectrum led to the discovery of the true nature of the stars.

Visible light makes up only a fraction of

the whole spectrum of wave lengths of energy. The next shorter waves beyond the visible violet are invisible ultraviolet waves, X-rays and gamma rays that are measured in trillionths of an inch. Longer than the visible reds are the invisible infrareds (which we feel as heat), microwaves, radar and radio waves, some that have wave lengths millions of miles long. Arranging all of these various forms of energy according to their wave lengths in a single sequence—the electromagnetic spectrum—was the work of many people over many years.

Out of this work and the atomic theory it led to, astronomy developed a new study: astrophysics. This science deals mainly with the chemical and physical nature of celestial bodies. As early as 1859 some of the sun's principal spectral lines had been identified with elements in its atmosphere. By 1871,

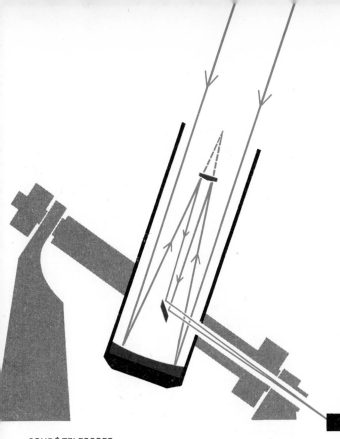

COUDÉ TELESCOPE

Inside Reflecting Telescopes

More advanced telescopes called reflectors work by bouncing light off mirrors instead of passing it through lenses. The type developed by Newton (*far left*) directs light from a curved mirror at the bottom of the tube to a focal point near the top, where it can be observed directly (if the telescope is big enough for a man to sit inside); or a small, flat mirror deflects it out through a hole in the tube's side. In the Cassegrainian telescope, light from the bottom mirror is reflected to a smaller curved mirror near the top, where it is aimed back through a hole in the bottom mirror to a focus below. The coudé arrangement works much the same but the rays are deflected with a third flat mirror to a spectrograph.

the English astronomer Sir Joseph Norman Lockyer announced the discovery of a new chemical element, unknown on earth. He christened it helium, "the sun element," from the Greek word *helios*, or sun. Fourteen years later, helium was found on earth, in association with radioactive substances.

Spectroscopes, instruments that break up "white" light into its component colors, were soon being used in every major observatory. The radiance of far-off stars, shattered into rainbows, revealed by their spectral lines the identity of atoms billions of miles away. Over the years, the spectral lines proved to hold quantities of other information too: the speed of a star moving toward or away from the solar system, the temperature of its surface, even the amount of invisible gas and dust drifting in space between the star and the earth.

In 1850, at about the same time as the invention of the spectroscope, photographic plates were first deliberately exposed to the stars by John Whipple at the Harvard College Observatory. Because they were permanent, reliable records, photographs soon replaced the sketches or written descriptions that were the only means astronomers had to record their observations until then.

But photography was even more useful than this. If an astronomer stares at a group of stars all night long, his eye senses no more light than it does in a wink. A photographic plate, on the contrary, gradually collects more and more information: where a 10-second exposure may reveal only 20 fairly bright stars, a 10-hour exposure may show 2,000 stars that are too faint to be seen by the human eye even when assisted by the finest telescope in the world.

31

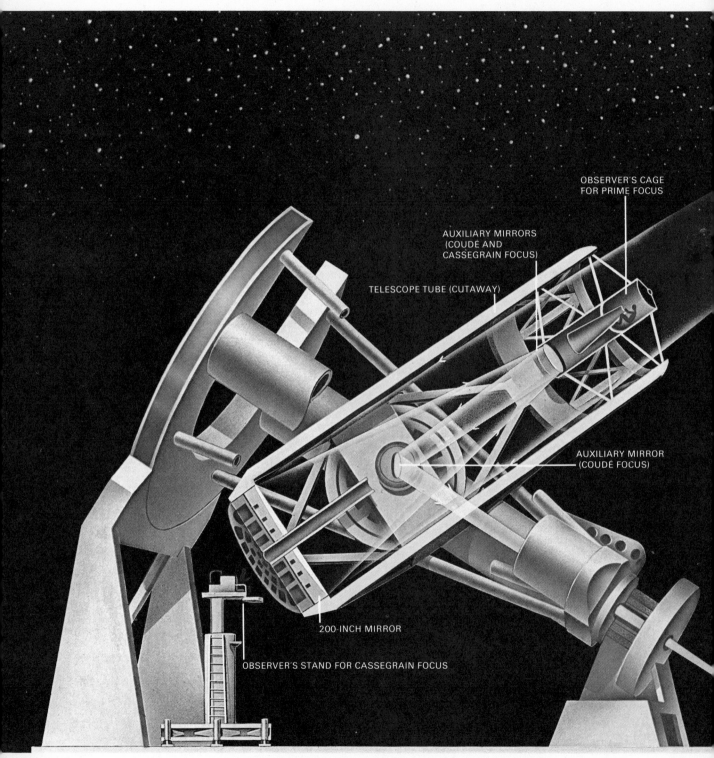

OBSERVER'S CAGE
FOR PRIME FOCUS

AUXILIARY MIRRORS
(COUDÉ AND
CASSEGRAIN FOCUS)

TELESCOPE TUBE (CUTAWAY)

AUXILIARY MIRROR
(COUDÉ FOCUS)

200-INCH MIRROR

OBSERVER'S STAND FOR CASSEGRAIN FOCUS

NORTH PIER

SOUTH PIER

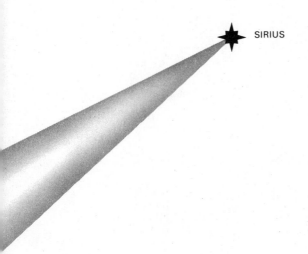

SIRIUS

Anatomy of a Giant

How one of the world's largest telescopes, the
Palomar reflector, works is shown in this cutaway
view. Light is gathered by the huge 200-inch
main mirror at the base of the telescope, directed
into a bright beam and then guided by two
smaller mirrors into a special room for spectrum
studies (*below*). This is done mainly at the
coudé focus. For direct observation of stars and
other objects in the sky, the telescope is used
with other mirror combinations. In the prime-focus
arrangement, light is concentrated toward the
instrument's upper end, where it may be recorded
directly on a photographic plate; this requires
that an observer ride in a cage inside the telescope.
The Cassegrain focus uses a small convex mirror
to reflect the beam of light back through a hole in
the main mirror to an instrument operated by
an observer on a high platform (*far left*).

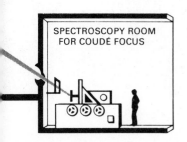

SPECTROSCOPY ROOM
FOR COUDÉ FOCUS

An even more far-reaching development
was the discovery of invisible radio waves
as a means of observing and charting the
skies. The first scientist to explore this field
was Karl Jansky at the Bell Telephone Lab-
oratories in the late 1920s and early 1930s.
All that young Jansky had to start with
was unexplained static in transoceanic ra-
diotelephones. His job was to find out where
the static came from so that the telephone
company could reduce it. But when the
source of the static proved difficult to pin-
point, Jansky invented something brand-
new to track it down. He built a radio
antenna 60 feet long—the first "radio telescope" in the world—and mounted it on
four old wheels on a circular cinder-block
track. By rotating this contraption and
carefully recording all the radio signals it received, he was able to divide the static of
one important short-wave frequency into
three categories: bangs from nearby thunderclaps, clicks from distant thunderclaps
—and a steady whisper from outer space.

Jansky's mysterious whisper turned out
to be the strong radio noise that emanates
from the nucleus of the Milky Way. Another young investigator, Grote Reber, took
up the challenge. Reber read Jansky's re-
port and by 1937 he was eavesdropping on
the universe with the aid of a 31-foot sheet-
metal dish he had assembled in his back-
yard. Reber confirmed that the nucleus of
the galaxy—invisible to optical telescopes
because it was hidden behind obscuring

(*Text continued on page 37*)

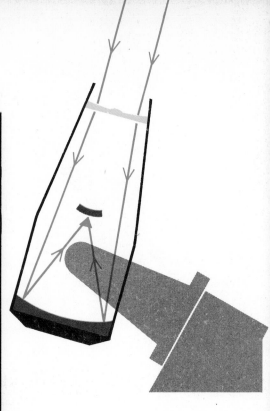

Companion Telescopes

The 200-inch Palomar reflector telescope, whose giant mirror structure is seen from its control room *(right)*, can penetrate deep into the outer skies. But its field of vision is very narrow. To map larger areas of the heavens, the Palomar observatory uses a telescope perfected by the German Bernhard Schmidt. The 48-inch Schmidt telescope *(diagram above)* has a wide-seeing spherical mirror. Light is first passed through a large, thin lens, bounced off the mirror, then focused on a curved photographic plate. The result can be seen at top left in a picture of a spiral galaxy. To examine the galaxy in detail, the Palomar reflector is zeroed in *(bottom left)*.

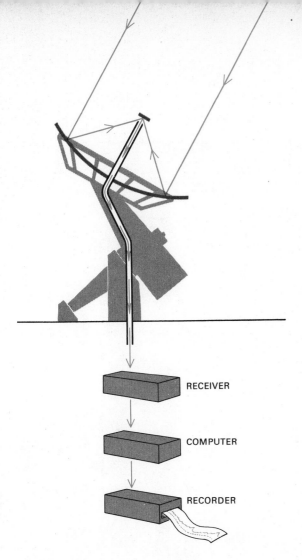

RECEIVER

COMPUTER

RECORDER

Tuning In on Space

A radio telescope is a huge instrument designed for collecting weak radio signals from faraway stars; it is also used for tracking spacecraft in their distant orbits. The type shown on these pages uses a large dish to concentrate the waves on the antenna, which is mounted above the center of the dish. The waves are first amplified by a receiver (above), then sent to a computer that sorts out the static. A recorder finally transcribes the signals on a graph. At left, this Goldstone radio telescope, which has an 85-foot antenna, stands in a lonely spot in the southern California sands 40 miles from Death Valley. Built in 1958 to track satellites, it has picked up faint radio signals from millions of miles away.

clouds of gas and dust—was a signal source. He also located several other "hot spots" in the sky that did not seem to coincide with any visible objects. His first reports were published in 1940. During World War II there were few opportunities to pursue these clues. But after the war, investigators around the world set up antennae and began gathering information. It soon was apparent that Jansky and Reber had founded a whole new field of study—radio astronomy.

Today radio astronomy is a full-fledged partner of optical astronomy. All over the world, antennae have been raised to gather in the celestial noises that make up the true "music of the spheres." For the fun of it, radio astronomers sometimes connect their instruments to loud-speakers so that they can hear the cosmic broadcasts as audible sound waves. They say that the Milky Way hisses incessantly, the sun sighs intermittently, and the planet Jupiter sends out a deep grumble that sounds as if it were the legendary voice of the ancient Roman thunder god himself. Usually, however, radio astronomers "listen" to the universe only through the graphs of signal intensity traced by their instruments. By marking radio "hot spots" on sky maps, they have gradually built up a picture of the radio heavens quite different from the picture of the optical heavens.

Beyond the solar system, radio telescopes cannot "hear" most real stars, but the clouds of cosmic gas and dust between the stars

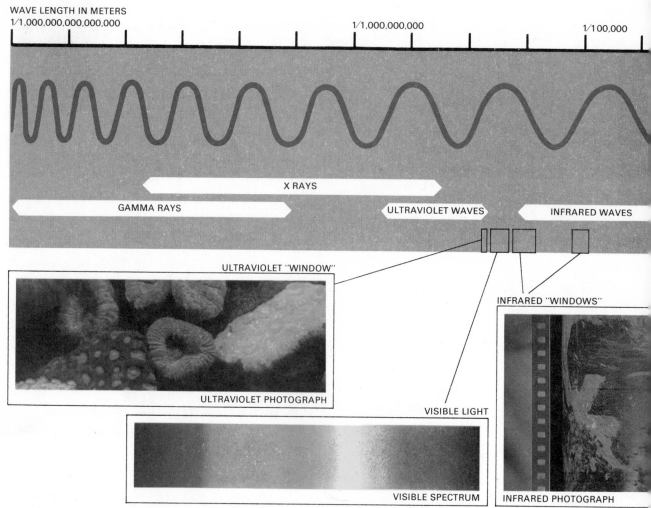

WAVE LENGTH IN METERS
1/1,000,000,000,000,000   1/1,000,000,000   1/100,000

X RAYS

GAMMA RAYS

ULTRAVIOLET WAVES

INFRARED WAVES

ULTRAVIOLET "WINDOW"

INFRARED "WINDOWS"

ULTRAVIOLET PHOTOGRAPH

VISIBLE LIGHT

VISIBLE SPECTRUM

INFRARED PHOTOGRAPH

emit radiation in a narrow band of wave lengths centered at about 21 centimeters, while other celestial objects give off signals at other frequencies. Most numerous of all cosmic radio sources are galaxies located beyond the Milky Way. Some of the galaxies from which radio emissions are received by the largest radio telescopes are estimated to be 10^{22} (10,000,000,000,000,000,000,000) miles away from the solar system.

The biggest part of a radio telescope is its antenna, or energy collector. The two main kinds of antenna are the dish and the dipole array. The dish is a large, shallow parabolic "mirror" of sheet metal or wire mesh. This gathers in radio energy and concentrates it on a small antenna at the point of focus, exactly the same way the mirror in a reflecting telescope collects light on the lens of an eyepiece. By contrast, the dipole array is a forest of many separate, identical antennae that collect energy by feeding all their weak individual signals into one common receiving set.

The dish antenna can be used at many wave lengths; the simple dipoles receive only

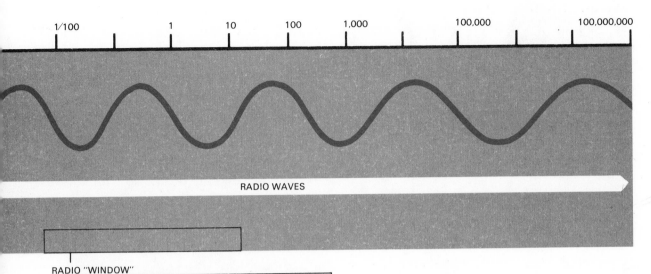

1/100   1   10   100   1,000   100,000   100,000,000

RADIO WAVES

RADIO "WINDOW"

WAVES OF RADIO LENGTH

Our "Windows" on the Universe

The electromagnetic spectrum, represented by the
wavy line in the graph above, includes everything
from deadly gamma rays a billionth of a millimeter
in length to radio waves over 60,000 miles long.
But only some of these waves reach the earth,
through the "windows" or gaps that allow visible
light waves and some infrared and radio waves to
penetrate our thick atmosphere. Photography has
widened the visible-light window into the ultraviolet
and infrared wave bands, and heat detectors record
other infrared waves. The pictures below the graph
illustrate what these wave lengths show us in more
familiar terms. From left to right, they show deep-
sea corals photographed in ultraviolet light; the
sun's spectrum, which includes all the colors we can
see; the earth giving off infrared rays, as recorded
by a satellite's heat-sensitive television camera; and
water rippling in waves as long as some of the
radio waves we receive but cannot photograph.

a narrow band of wave lengths, depending
on the length and spacing of their metal
rods. But dipoles are easy to put up, and
hundreds or even thousands of them, spaced
out in grids or crosses over acres of land,
can collect the energy on one wave length
with precision. In some telescopes the dipoles can be rotated and tilted together to
point in more than one direction. In others
they are fixed and can "listen" only in the
direction in which the spinning, orbiting
earth aims them. However, in the course
of a year any point on earth has a substan-

39

tial fraction of the sky directly overhead, so fixed dipole arrays can be extremely useful for comprehensive sky surveys. Movable dish antennae, on the other hand, can show the exact, or nearly exact, direction of a radio source. Dish antennae also can be used to fix the position of celestial objects.

The great drawback of dish antennae is the cost and difficulty of building them. One of the largest fully steerable dishes yet constructed is the 250-foot radio mirror at Jodrell Bank, near Manchester, England. This monster rotates to any part of the compass and rocks up and down on a gigantic yoke that keeps it aimed precisely even in high winds and heavy rains. In the United States a partially movable antenna 300 feet in diameter is in use at Green Bank, West Virginia. But the world's most powerful radio telescope by far is the huge dish, 1,000 feet from rim to rim, near the town of Arecibo, Puerto Rico. Cradled in a natural hollow in the land, the Arecibo an-

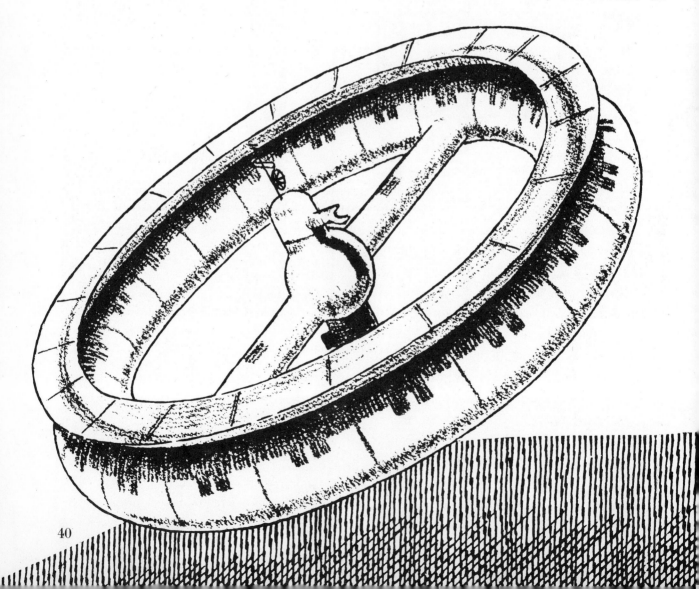

Going beyond the Atmosphere

The earth's atmosphere causes distortions in light
waves that make a crystal-clear view of the heavens
impossible. The only way to get a clear view is
to send instruments into space by means of balloons
(*above*), rockets and satellites, or spacecraft. One
future proposal is a space station 250 feet in diameter
(*left*), which would wheel above the atmosphere with
astronomers and their telescopes on board.

41

tenna is made up of 19 acres of steel mesh.

As optical telescopes are often troubled by city lights and smog, so radio telescopes are beset by man-made interference such as radio and television broadcasts. To weed out these unwanted signals, radio astronomers feed the impulses from their antennae into powerful amplifiers. These usually feed, in turn, into computers for sorting out the random space noises from the nonrandom noises caused by human beings.

Largest of all the problems facing radio astronomers is pinpointing the direction of what they "hear." Radio telescopes receive waves 1,000 to 100 million times longer than the waves of visible light. As a result, the size of radio telescopes would have to be enormous to get results as exact as those of optical telescopes. Even the immense dish at Arecibo is only 60 times as wide as the 200-inch Hale telescope at Palomar. To separate two close radio sources of medium wave lengths as sharply as the Palomar telescope can separate the images of two close stars, a radio telescope would need to have a dish wider than the moon.

Scanning the Southern Skies

In Australia, a large radio telescope raises its grid to the southern skies, gathering signals from distant galaxies. Nearer stars, visible to the eye or to optical instruments, wheel slowly around the South Pole, which is located exactly at the center of their curved trails on this 90-minute time exposure.

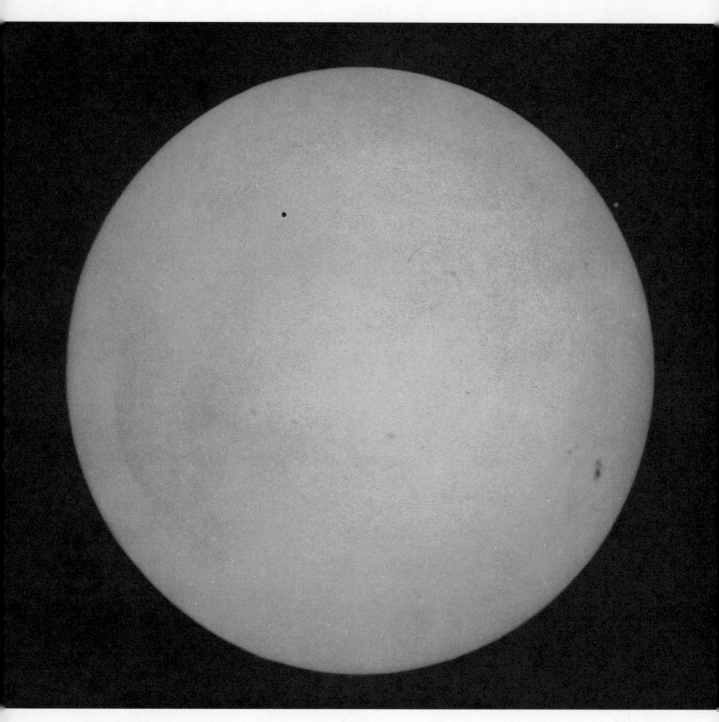

TINY MERCURY, the smallest planet and the one
closest to the sun, appears as a tiny black dot
(*upper left*) against the immense disk of the sun.
The other dark specks are sunspots, cooler eddies
in a seething sea of light. These are sometimes as
much as twice the size of our entire planet.

3

Planets, Asteroids and Comets

The principal proving ground for cosmic theories has been—and will long remain—the nearby regions of space within the gravitational realm of the sun. Although the solar system is a tiny sample of the total universe, it includes a surprisingly broad sample of the dynamic structures and forces of the universe at large.

The solar system includes one star—the sun—nine planets, 32 moons, some 50,000 asteroids and perhaps 100 billion comets, plus countless dust specks, gas molecules and free atoms—atoms not in a molecular pattern. A full 99.86 per cent of the solar system's substance is tied up in the sun.

The word "planet" comes from the Greek *planetai*, which means "wanderers" and refers to the erratic way in which the planets seem to drift among the fixed stars. Because the earth rotates on its axis and revolves around the sun, the distant stars appear to us to move in regular daily and yearly cycles. Naturally, the nearby planets share this effect, called *apparent* motion, but they are so close to us that we can also see their *real* motions around the sun. The combination of their apparent motions and their real motions makes the planets' paths across the sky seem irregular and confusing, compared with the steady cycles the stars follow. Venus, for instance, takes 140 days less than the earth does to circle around the sun. In so doing, it often passes the earth on its shorter orbit and appears, as it pulls ahead and rounds the turn, to slow down, stop and then go backward.

In addition to having different speeds around the sun, most of the planets move in orbits that have different tilts. This means that we generally see the orbits of the other planets from slightly above or below. It also means that when the other planets pass in front of or behind the sun they seldom cross the sun's surface or disappear behind it, but seem to sweep a little above or below it. Mercury "transits" the sun—or crosses in front of it—some 13 times each century. Venus crosses twice every 130 years. The other planets, because they circle outside the earth's orbit, do not cross the sun's face at all but occasionally disappear behind it.

Mercury, perhaps the smallest planet and the closest to the sun, comes within 29 million miles of the sun at one end of its elliptical orbit and swings out to 43 million miles at the other end. The period of each revolution is equal to only 88 days on Earth, and Mercury rotates on its axis in such a way that its "day" is actually longer than its "year." A point on Mercury's equator receives sunlight for 88 consecutive earth days and is then plunged into darkness for 88 days. While the side of the planet facing out toward space is being frozen, the side facing the sun is being cooked to temperatures that may approach 1,000° F. Probably no man will ever visit Mercury, but should some well-insulated astronaut land there, he would not need much fuel to take off again. The mass of the planet is only one eighteenth of the earth's and its gravitational pull only three eighths of the earth's. This means that instead of having to blast off at seven miles per second—the earth's escape velocity—the visitor would need a speed of only 2.6 miles per second.

The planet next closest to the sun, and closest of all to the earth, is Venus. Not only does it have an atmosphere, but this atmosphere is topped about 20 miles above the surface by an unbroken quilt of yellowish white clouds. This cloud layer is so impenetrable that not until the early 1960s did scientists first determine the length of a day on Venus. Using radar astronomy, they found that Venus completed a rotation only once in every 243 earth days. Since it takes Venus 224.7 earth days to go around the sun, the combined motions make sunrise take place on Venus at intervals of about 118 earth days. In many ways, Venus strikingly resembles the earth. Its mass is 81 per cent, its volume 88 per cent, its density 93 per cent and its escape velocity 92 per cent that of the earth.

Scientists' ideas of what lies beneath the cloud layer of Venus began to be confirmed in October 1967, when within less than a day, the Russian capsule Venus 4 crash-

The Sun's Family

The sun's nine satellites, or planets, and their own satellites, or moons, are shown here in their relative sizes and in the order in which they circle the sun *(seen at bottom)*. Brightly colored Jupiter and ringed Saturn have 22 of the moons, while the seven smaller planets claim only 10 among them. Three of the planets— Mercury, Venus and Pluto—have no moons at all. Next to the names of the planets are their symbols, most of them invented in ancient times. These symbols are used as a kind of shorthand by astronomers today.

landed on the planet and the U.S. spaceship Mariner 5 flew close by it. Their observations and those of later Russian and American craft indicated that Venus' atmosphere has a pressure 90 times greater than the earth's, and is composed mainly of carbon dioxide with traces of water but little free oxygen. In the cloud layer, temperatures may range as low as −40° F., but on the ground they rise to around 900° F.

After the earth, the next planet out from the sun—and the only other planet that may support life—is Mars, 142 million miles from the sun. Mars is small, only one tenth the size of Earth, and its average temperature is about −60° F. Its air is extremely thin because the escape velocity is only three miles per second, less than half that of the earth. The atmosphere seems to contain some water vapor but is mostly carbon dioxide. The permanent northern polar cap of Mars, however, is composed entirely of frozen water and becomes larger in the Martian winter when the carbon dioxide, known on Earth as dry ice, freezes over it. A year on Mars is 687½ earth days long and its day lasts a little over 24½ earth hours. Mars has two tiny satellites or moons, Phobos and Deimos, one of them seven and the other five miles in diameter.

Man has long suspected that there may be life on Mars, and in July 1976 a dramatic step was taken in an effort to check out the theory. California's Jet Propulsion Laboratory successfully landed the unmanned Viking 1 spacecraft on Mars's Chryse Planitia (Gold Plain), and in two hours scientists were studying the first photographs shot on the surface of the Red Planet. The pictures revealed a flat, rock-strewn plain a little like the desert areas of Arizona and Mexico.

Viking carried other instruments, to sample the atmosphere, register temperatures, and record wind velocities, barometric pressures and humidity. There was also a seismograph to detect ground tremors. The most important instrument was a minilab that would analyze soil samples for signs of life. Even before landing, Viking's instruments had detected nitrogen and argon in the atmosphere: nitrogen is an element essential to living terrestrial organisms on Earth, and argon suggests that Mars once had an atmosphere more likely to encourage life.

A few weeks later a second craft, Viking 2, landed on Mars's Utopia Planitia (Utopia Plain), almost halfway around the planet from Viking 1. Viking 2's mission: to duplicate its sister craft's experiments in a damper, potentially more fertile region of Mars.

For the next 340 million miles outward from the sun, space is empty except for the small, rough islands of rock and metal known as asteroids, which all together total less than 5 per cent of the moon in mass (the moon's mass is less than 1.25 per cent of the earth's). The first, and biggest, asteroid was discovered on the first night of the 19th Century by the Italian astronomer Giuseppe Piazzi. He watched it for 41 evenings and then lost it. The mathematical genius Karl Friedrich Gauss gave up all his

The Phases of Venus

Through an astronomer's telescope Venus is seen to go through phases just as the moon does. When it is on the far side of the sun from the earth, the planet's full face is lighted *(left)*. But as Venus overtakes us and moves between the sun and the earth, it appears to dwindle to a crescent *(right)*.

other work and from Piazzi's scanty observations reconstructed the lost body's orbit. When he emerged from his figuring a few weeks later, he told astronomers where to point their telescopes. They did and sure enough, there was the lost wanderer. Piazzi named it Ceres; it is an island of jagged rock, 480 miles in diameter with a surface area of 700,000 square miles.

Other asteroids were discovered in quick order: Pallas, 300 miles wide, in 1802; 120-mile Juno in 1804; 240-mile Vesta in 1807. Today about 30,000 sizable asteroids are believed to exist, ranging from Ceres down to Icarus, which is only a mile in diameter. The number of still-smaller asteroids—the size of boulders, pebbles or sand grains—is estimated in the billions. Only some 1,600 have been named; they and another 1,500 are watched carefully enough so that their orbits can be plotted and predictions made about their future whereabouts. Discovering them has become easy and routine. When an astronomer trains a powerful telescope on a section of the sky that is expected to contain asteroids, and the automatic movements of its mount are adjusted to the average speed of the asteroids, these faint bodies will slowly begin to burn themselves in as pale dots on the astronomer's photographic film or plate. The stars, which do not move with the telescopes, will appear as streaks of light on the film. But ignoring streaks and plotting orbits for the dots is not easy, and astronomers are usually too busy with

Seeing the Earth from Space

In the photograph at left, taken by a spacecraft 240,000 miles from the earth, the edge of the moon looms large in the right foreground; the earth itself looks like a far-off "moon," with half its face shining in the sunlight, the other half darkened by night.

Above is a picture of the earth taken from a satellite 6,600 miles high, showing patterns formed by the earth's atmosphere. Swirling masses of clouds veil the broad Pacific Ocean, but the continent of Australia stands out clearly at the bottom. At the top, a blanket of clouds covers part of Alaska and extends out over the Bering Sea to Siberia.

Is There Life on Mars?

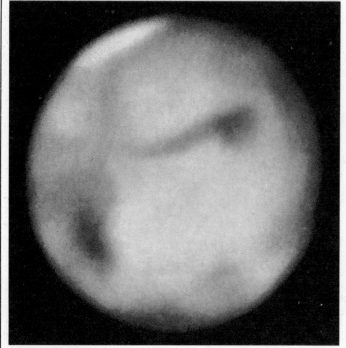

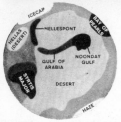

THE FACES OF MARS, seen rotating through its 24½-hour day, are shown in these pre-Viking photographs of the planet. The light regions are desertlike areas; the bright sliver at top is a polar icecap.

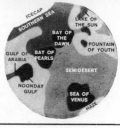

THE "SEAS" OF MARS, the dark areas to which the early astronomers gave fanciful names, are not seas at all. Most of the visible water on Mars appears as atmospheric vapor or ice locked in polar caps.

more distant matters to bother with them.

All the 3,000-odd asteroids that have been tracked revolve around the sun counterclockwise, in the same direction as the planets. Most asteroids move in a broad band between Mars and Jupiter.

Jupiter's strong gravitational field sometimes knocks one of the asteroids out of its normal orbit on a voyage down toward the sun or up toward the outer planets. Icarus' present orbit takes it twice as close to the sun as Mercury. Other asteroids often come

uncomfortably close to Earth. Eros—a cigar-shaped rock 15 miles long and five miles wide that tumbles end over end as it circles the sun—can come within a scant 14 million miles of the earth. Amor, Icarus, Apollo and Adonis can pass even closer. In 1937 Hermes came as close as 500,000 miles—only twice as far as the moon.

Out-of-orbit asteroids sometimes collide with the earth. Of the boulder-sized ones, called meteorites, about 1,500 strike each year. Full-fledged asteroids are thought to

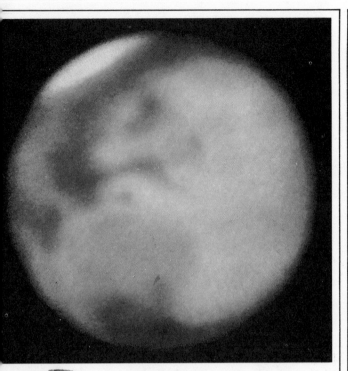

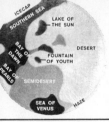

LIFE ON MARS, if it exists, is primitive. Many astronomers thought lichens or other low life forms might cause the color changes in dark areas called "seas," but Viking's cameras found no obvious life signs.

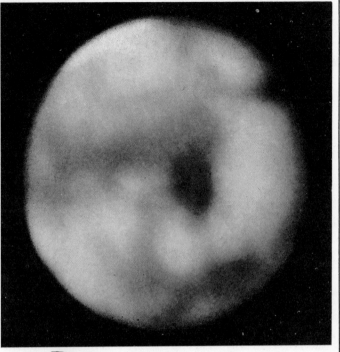

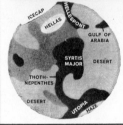

A MARTIAN "CANAL," the curving band near the bottom of this picture, was given the name Thothnepenthes (*see diagram*). Viking's orbital pictures revealed numerous dry "riverbeds" and valleys.

strike much less frequently, perhaps once every 10,000 years. When they do, they cause an explosion that leaves a large pit or crater. Geologists have recently begun to recognize the "astroblemes," or "star wounds," that they inflict on the earth's surface; it seems likely that only the shield of the atmosphere and the healing power of vegetation, erosion and mountain-building have kept the earth from being as pock-marked as the moon.

Beyond Mars and the asteroids, Jupiter—

484 million miles away from the sun—is of such size and materials that it seems to belong to a different order from the other planets. Jupiter's volume is more than 1,400 times Earth's. Its mass is more than twice that of all the other eight planets put together. It has an atmosphere thousands of miles deep, held by a gravity 2.64 times stronger than Earth's. Instead of being a sphere of rock and metal like the four inner planets, Jupiter is composed mainly of

(*Text continued on page 57*)

The Centaur stage ignited briefly *(left)*, jettisoning the Titan stage two and setting the craft into a temporary orbit around the Earth. A blast gave a push toward Mars and the Orbiter-Lander was ejected *(above)*, solar panels extended, and the protective cap was discarded. After the spacecraft coasted 460 million miles, rockets turned it *(above, right)*, so when the engine fired, the craft entered a Mars orbit.

Some 150,000 feet above Earth, Titan's second stage fired as the first stage was jettisoned, and shrouds protecting the Centaur stage dropped away.

The Titan III/Centaur launch vehicle, lifting away from Earth, was powered by solid fuel boosters, which were discarded as Titan's main engines fired.

Multiple Maneuvers to Reach a Far-off Planet

The complexity of the 1976 Mars mission is illustrated by this sequential drawing, which shows the Viking's metamorphosis from streamlined launch vehicle to spidery Mars Lander. The most difficult portion of the 11-month, 460 million-mile voyage came when the Lander, separated from its parent ship, the Orbiter, began its descent through Mars's atmosphere. Because the Lander was then so far from Earth, commands beamed to the craft took a painfully long 20 minutes to reach it. To avoid delays in controlling the craft during the landing sequence illustrated at the lower right, the preprogramed computer that was aboard the Lander took command, deploying the parachute and firing braking rockets in order to enable the Lander to settle softly on Mars.

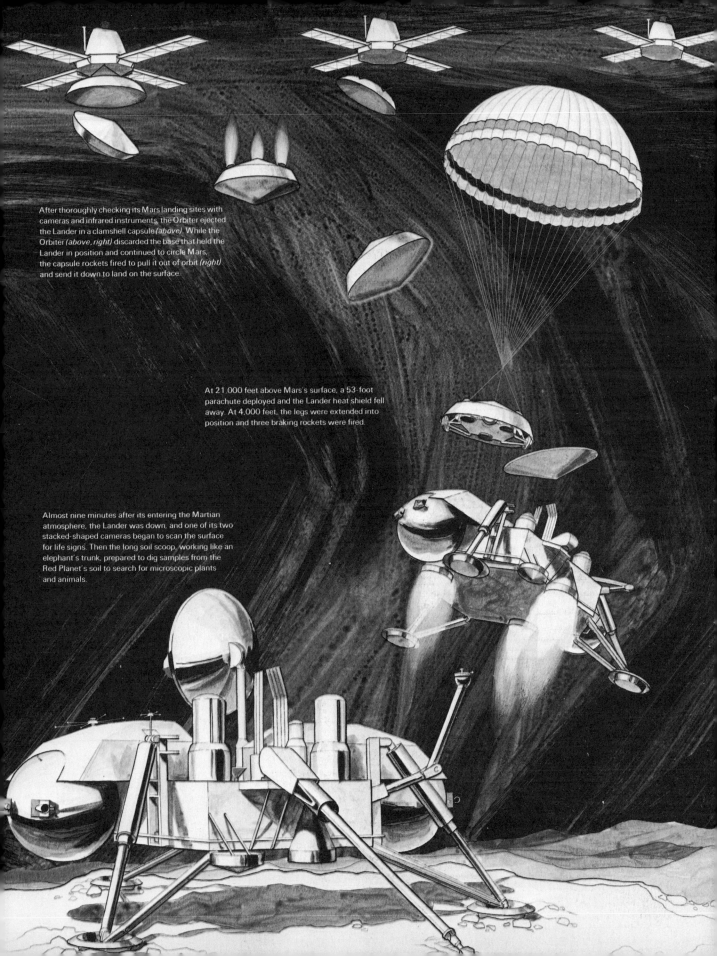

After thoroughly checking its Mars landing sites with cameras and infrared instruments, the Orbiter ejected the Lander in a clamshell capsule *(above)*. While the Orbiter *(above, right)* discarded the base that held the Lander in position and continued to circle Mars, the capsule rockets fired to pull it out of orbit *(right)* and send it down to land on the surface.

At 21,000 feet above Mars's surface, a 53-foot parachute deployed and the Lander heat shield fell away. At 4,000 feet, the legs were extended into position and three braking rockets were fired.

Almost nine minutes after its entering the Martian atmosphere, the Lander was down, and one of its two stacked-shaped cameras began to scan the surface for life signs. Then the long soil scoop, working like an elephant's trunk, prepared to dig samples from the Red Planet's soil to search for microscopic plants and animals.

A Stormy Giant of a Planet

Jupiter (*left*), the largest planet, is more than 11 times as broad as the earth (*above*). It is so cold that its atmosphere of poisonous gases contains clouds of ammonia crystals. This atmosphere, which may be a violent one of torrential rains and titanic blizzards, is marked by shifting colored bands. The most famous marking is the "Great Red Spot," the pinkish area toward the lower right in this photograph. The spot changes color from red to gray and sometimes disappears for years at a time.

light substances such as hydrogen, ammonia and methane—all of which are gases on Earth. Possibly Jupiter's innermost core is of rock and metal, but it may be hydrogen squeezed into a heavy, metallic state by the overwhelming weight of Jupiter's outer layers—a pressure equivalent to tens of millions times the earth's atmospheric pressure.

In spite of its monstrous size and mass, Jupiter has a low density—only a quarter of the earth's. And this bloated giant whirls in a day only nine hours and 50 minutes long. And yet, Jupiter with its 12 satellites—two of them bigger than the earth's moon—revolves around the sun at 8.1 miles a second, so slowly that one of its years is 11.9 earth years long.

The atmospheric turbulence caused by Jupiter's rotation is immense. Streaks of colored gases trace visible lines across the planet's face. A huge red spot, wider than the earth is around, has hovered for at least a century just south of Jupiter's equator. Another feature of the planet's stormy outer layers is a set of violent radiation belts around its equator; these pour forth short-wave radio signals that reach the earth, some 400 million miles away, often stronger than those from any other object in the sky.

Even more extreme than Jupiter is Saturn, a huge gaseous world 95 times as massive as the earth but only seven tenths as dense as water. Saturn revolves around the sun once every 29.5 earth years at a distance of 887 million miles, almost double

An Ice-ringed Planet

Particles of ice or frosted gravel whirl around Saturn's equator in a ring system 42,000 miles wide. The bands in the ring are only a few inches thick; the innermost is too thin to be seen in the photograph at left. The painting at right shows how Saturn might look from Mimas, one of its satellites. The colored streaks on the planet's surface are atmospheric belts like Jupiter's; the wide shadow is cast by the rings, seen here edge on. A thousand times as big as the earth, Saturn is made of such loosely packed matter that it could float in water.

Jupiter's distance from the sun. It spins its light materials fast, in a day of just 10 hours and 14 minutes. Its bulging equator is girdled by four rings of snow and grit, extending from 6,000 to 48,000 miles above its surface in a disk that is only a few inches thick. Beyond the rings—which are thought to be a sort of unformed moon— Saturn also has 10 conventional satellites. The largest, Titan, is as big as Mercury, as orange as Mars, and is the only satellite of any planet known to have an atmosphere. Saturn's five inner satellites also are interesting: at least two of them appear to be smooth spheres of pure ice. Of the satellites that lie beyond Titan, the outermost,

Phoebe, is one of six in the entire solar system that revolve in a direction opposite to the rotation of their planets.

Saturn is the last of the five planets known from ancient times and visible to the naked eye. Nine hundred million miles beyond it, at twice Saturn's distance from the sun, lies the chill world of Uranus, which William Herschel first identified as a planet in 1781. Uranus, whose atmosphere is made up primarily of methane, is 14.5 times as massive as the earth. Its temperature is at least 270°F. below zero, its year is 84 earth years long, and it rotates every 10 hours and 49 minutes. The most surprising thing

about living on Uranus, if one could ever do such a thing, would be its seasons. Uranus' equator is tilted 98 degrees out of the plane of its orbit, compared to only 23.5 degrees for Earth and equally small or smaller angles for most of the other planets. This means that, at one side of its orbit, Uranus' south polar regions receive all the little warmth the distant sun provides; at the other side of its orbit, 42 years later, the north pole gets the sun. During the 42-year-long dark period at one of the poles a resident could see as many as five satellites in the sky at once, as well as many stars.

Neptune, the planet beyond Uranus, is nearly 2.8 billion miles from the sun. It was discovered as a direct result of Isaac Newton's celestial mechanics. Within 60 years of Uranus' discovery, astronomers noticed irregularities in that planet's orbit and concluded that an unseen planet beyond must be causing the disturbance. In the 1840s mathematicians calculated where this unknown planet should lie. In 1846 an astronomer pointed a telescope in the suggested direction and found Neptune within half an hour. It turned out to be a pale green orb, circling the sun once every 165 years. Two satellites travel with Neptune, one of which, named Triton, is both bigger and closer than the earth's moon.

Pluto, the ninth planet, was also dis-

INNER PLANETS

OUTER PLANETS

ASTEROIDS

COMETS

JUPITER

SATURN

URANUS

PLUTO

NEPTUNE

SUN

MERCURY

VENUS

EARTH

MARS

JUPITER

Blueprint of the Solar System

The orbits of the nine planets and of two comets are represented in the large diagram at left. The planets circle the sun in about the same plane, except Pluto, which has a sharply tilted orbit. The comets follow elliptical orbits that may carry them to the outermost fringes of the solar system and can take millions of years to complete. The enlarged section of the diagram (*box*) shows the inner four planets, as well as some of the many asteroids that circle the sun in various planes between Mars and Jupiter. All of the planets and asteroids orbit in a counterclockwise direction, viewed from the north.

covered as the result of prediction. But when it was found in 1930, it was so much smaller than expected that the discovery may simply have been an accident. Pluto is a tiny sphere, apparently a little larger than Mercury, and so distant that it is 700 times fainter than Neptune. It orbits eccentrically between 4.6 and 2.7 billion miles from the sun. Its year is 248 earth years, its temperature is $-400°$ F., and it has no satellites. Because Pluto's eccentric orbit swings inside Neptune's, bringing it as much as 35 million miles closer to the sun than Neptune, many astronomers consider Pluto a former satellite that Neptune lost in the early days of the solar system.

Beyond the nine planets, about 100 billion comets roam the icy edges of the solar system. They move not only in flat, oval orbits like the planets but also in a spherical halo surrounding the solar system and reaching out 10 trillion miles or more toward the sun's neighboring stars. Few of these comets have ever come close enough for astronomers to study them. Those that have indicate that a comet is merely an accumulation of frozen gases and grit, no more than a few miles in diameter, with a density much less than that of water.

Off by itself in space, a comet has no tail. But when it approaches the sun, solar energy vaporizes its outer layers to form a swollen head and a glaring tail pointing out toward space. The comet may now occupy a space larger than the sun, but comets

61

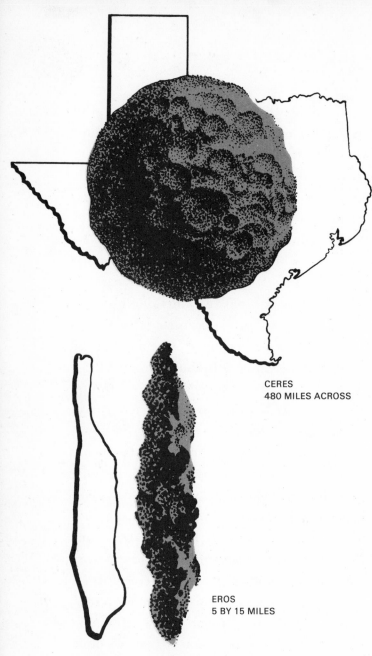

CERES
480 MILES ACROSS

EROS
5 BY 15 MILES

Giant Asteroids

The asteroids that orbit the sun between Mars and Jupiter range in size from specks of dust to miniature planets like Ceres *(top)*, over half as wide as Texas. Some 30,000 are a mile or more across, and there are billions of smaller ones. Cigar-shaped Eros *(above)*, about the size of Manhattan Island, whirls end over end, circling the sun on a path that takes it within 14 million miles of the earth. Asteroids that blaze into our atmosphere are known as meteors; those that strike the earth are called meteorites.

are such bucketfuls of nothing that they weigh not even a millionth of a billionth as much. The Great Comet of 1843 had a tail that streamed out more than 500 million miles. Halley's comet, returning to visibility every 76 years, is so brilliant that it has been recorded in Chinese and Japanese writings every time but once since 240 B.C.

Edmund Halley (1656-1742) was the first to state that comets are members of the solar system, traveling in elliptical orbits. Most of them are probably original members of the sun's family that have orbited around it since the solar system began. What causes one of them to leave its cold, chaotic realm and penetrate the heart of the solar system is probably the passing of some nearby star whose gravitational pull "kicks" the comet out of orbit. Once it is in among the planets, the comet may simply pass through without a collision and rocket back to its own regions, returning again only when its "year," several million years long, is up. Or the influence of a major planet may kick it into a new orbit that brings it close to the sun, again and again, until it disintegrates.

The fate of comets that play too often with the sun's fire is illustrated by the short and wild career of Biela's comet. It was first noticed hurtling in from space in 1772. After cutting its first close caper with the sun, it began reappearing in the sun's vicinity at regular six-and-a-half-year intervals. On its swing of 1846, it abruptly became two comets moving side by side. It put in one more appearance in its split form in 1852 and then vanished. Astronomers were still looking for it 20 years later when the whole of Europe was suddenly treated to a shower of meteors burning up as they entered the earth's atmosphere. The rain of cosmic sparks increased as it moved west. By the time it reached England, people could see a hundred blazing meteors a minute. Over the Atlantic, the display gradually diminished so that New Yorkers, at midnight, saw only a luminous drizzle. Careful calculations have since proved that the meteors were really the remains of Biela's comet crossing the earth's orbit just in time to meet the earth.

If a comet does collide with the earth before it has been eroded and broken up by the influence of the sun, it can pack a surprising punch for such an airy object. On June 30, 1908, a tremendous explosion rocked the forests along the Tunguska River in Siberia. Trees were toppled like dominoes out to more than 30 miles from the blast center. People were knocked over, and windowpanes blew in at a distance of 100 miles. An engineer 400 miles away brought his train to a shrill halt as the tracks of the Trans-Siberian Railway heaved and quaked before his eyes. What had caused the explosion long remained a mystery. Finally, in 1960 the Russian scientist Vassily Fesenkov announced it had been the head of a comet. He put its diameter at sev-

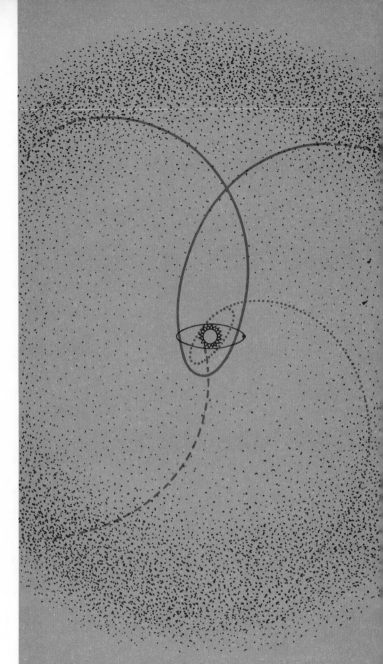

Runaway Comets

Comets, which orbit in a huge, spherical halo more than 12 billion miles from the sun, are occasionally "kicked" out of their tracks by the gravitational attraction of a star. When this happens, a comet can be wrenched by a large planet into a new, smaller orbit around the sun, like Halley's comet (*dotted line*), or it can make one big loop around the sun (*solid line*) and return to the halo. Or it can be dragged so deep inside the solar system (*broken line*) that the sun's energy soon vaporizes it.

eral miles and its weight at about a million tons. The whole spectacular incident had been set off by a small comet that was only about a millionth as heavy as similar ones roaming the solar system. But in its orbit it had met the earth almost head on, at a speed of 25 miles per second.

Such major accidents that overtake the earth along its highway in the sky overshadow the enormous numbers of lesser collisions that are really more important. The earth smashes into about 100 million shooting stars and uncounted billions of tiny meteorites every day. All of these "micrometeorites" are mere specks of dust, left over from the disintegration of comets or asteroids. But, all together, they add more than four million tons of matter to the earth each year. Since the earth was formed, this amounts to a skin some 10 feet deep all over its surface. It means that much of what the farmer plows today is ancient star dust, mixed and milled for thousands of years by the wind and rain.

A Comet's Periodic Splendor

Halley's Comet streams a tail 50 million miles long
as it streaks between the earth and Venus on May
13, 1910. One of the largest comets known, Halley's
appears every 75 to 76 years, and all its visits but
one have been recorded since 240 B.C. It will blaze
its way across our skies again in 1986.

4

The Nuclear Furnace of the Sun

The heart of the solar system—the source of its energy and principal motions, its brightest light and its sustainer of life—is, of course, the sun. And though we now know that it is merely one medium-sized star among billions, it is still a star—a marvelous giant totally different from the planets or comets that hurtle around it.

The sun, with an 864,000-mile diameter, includes a volume a thousand times that of the largest planet, and all its two billion billion billion tons are gas. Even under the crushing pressure at the core, its atoms still remain in a gaseous state, maintaining their ability to wander freely in spite of the unbelievable pressure put on them. What keeps the sun's core from condensing into a solid state is sheer energy—stupendous floods of energy that create an internal temperature of 25,000,000° F., heating not only the sun's enormous envelope of gas but the rest of the solar system as well. The source of this energy is in the slow, steady, destruction of the sun's substance by the nuclear fusion of hydrogen atoms into helium atoms. The process is a close cousin to the explosive reaction in an H-

67

bomb, except that its violence is cushioned by the quadrillions of cubic miles of elastic gas that surround the sun's core.

This nuclear reaction transforms 657 million tons of solar hydrogen into 652.5 million tons of helium ash every second. The missing 4.5 million tons have been converted into energy, mainly in the form of gamma rays.

This energy works its way to the sun's surface and then radiates out into space. If it did not, the sun would very quickly grow so hot that it would explode. Because we are able to measure the sunshine that is intercepted by the earth, we are able to calculate the total output of solar energy. It turns out that the sun shines with a constant power of 495.4 million billion billion watts—which is many billion times the generating capacity of all the power plants in the United States.

If the immense energy released at the sun's core reached the surface all in the form of gamma waves, the result would be a death ray spreading throughout the solar system. But these rays are softened in passing through the blanket of gaseous atoms outside the core. A gamma ray packs millions of times as much energy as a ray of visible light; it can split an atom's nucleus apart. More often, however, it spends part of its force rattling the atom's electrons in their orbits. If it hits the nucleus or knocks an electron loose, the gamma ray changes into one of several other rays, each with less energy and longer wave length.

On their way to the sun's surface, gamma rays pass through several different layers. In the densest layer, next to the core, some

gamma rays are changed into X-rays and ultraviolet rays. Next, this thermonuclear energy charges through a thick layer of less tightly packed atoms. This gaseous mass disperses some of the energy in violent motion. At the base of this region, the gas begins to boil, driving hot currents 80,000 miles up to the visible surface of the sun— the photosphere. Like water boiling in a pot, most of this gas is drawn back to the bottom, but some of it spurts 3,000 miles above the surface before splashing down. This region of fiery spray is the sun's lower atmosphere, or chromosphere.

Partly tamed by its passage through the outer layers of the sun, this energy is subdued even more in the chromosphere. For us, the earth's own atmosphere acts as still another shield or a filter, permitting only parts of the whole energy spectrum to reach us and the instruments we aim at the sun. Even weakened by all these effects, however, the sun's radiance remains too strong to be looked at directly or photographed like a planet or a far-off star. To study the sun without going blind, an observer must watch its reflection projected on a screen. Looking directly at the sun, even through dark sunglasses, can cause permanent damage to the eyes. Looking directly at the sun through binoculars or a telescope will cause blindness, because the lenses concentrate its powerful rays into the eye just as a magnifying glass would. As every Boy Scout knows, a magnifying glass can be used to start a fire by focusing the sun's rays on a pile of dead leaves.

A Long Tube for Sun-Watching

The strange-looking device in the photograph at left is a solar telescope atop Kitt Peak in Arizona. Since the telescope is fixed, it has a movable mirror that follows the sun. To provide a large image of the sun, the light is reflected 500 feet to another mirror at the bottom of the tube, then reflected 300 feet back to a third mirror. Finally the light is sent into a spectrograph used by astronomers to learn the chemical and physical makeup of the sun.

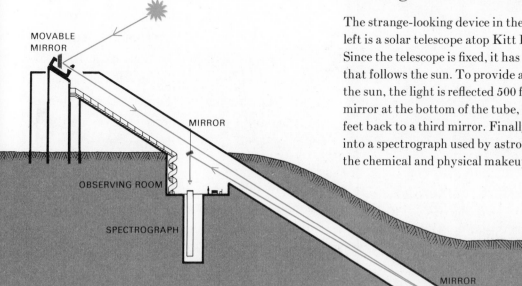

MOVABLE MIRROR

MIRROR

OBSERVING ROOM

SPECTROGRAPH

MIRROR

The Sun's Revealing Spectrum

This strip of photographs more than 40 feet long, taken by a spectrograph, forms a complete spectrum of the sun. To scientists like the expert above, the spectral lines on the film reveal physical conditions in the sun's atmosphere—temperature, pressure, magnetic fields, amounts of chemical elements.

For such reasons, telescopes designed for observing the sun are totally different from those used to observe stars or planets. With the sun, the aim is *not* to collect as much light as possible but instead to obtain an image as large and detailed as possible. This can be done only by special telescopes with long focal lengths. One of the largest of these is the 500-foot-long apparatus on 6,875-foot Kitt Peak near Tucson, Arizona, which can project an image of the sun nearly a yard in diameter. The business end of the solar telescope slants up more than 100 feet above the ground. The rest is all underground. At the top, a flat 80-inch mirror, electrically driven, follows the sun across the sky and reflects its image down into the heart of the telescope 500 feet away. There a second mirror, a curved one 60 inches across, focuses the image 300 feet back up the shaft to a third mirror, which sends the sunlight into an underground observation room. From the screen in the observation room the sun's image can be taken and broken up into all its thousands of wave lengths. From spectrograms of these wave lengths the materials of the sun's photosphere can be analyzed almost as exactly as if they were samples in a laboratory.

These methods have already taught astronomers a great amount about the sun's surface. Sixty-seven of the 92 known natural elements found on the earth also have been recognized in the sun. These elements exist in roughly 25,000 different states of internal arrangements, as well as in all sorts of strangely ionized forms—with excesses or scarcities of electrons—that would not survive for a second under the conditions that prevail on the earth.

These unstable forms of matter are symptoms of the general unrest on the sun. Even the sun's rotation in space is not uniform. Since they are not rigid, the great sphere's gases do not move in unison. A point on the rim of the sun's equator completes one turn every 25 days, while a point near the poles takes a full 35 days. This uneven rotation, coupled with electric disturbances caused by intense heat, keeps the sun in continual magnetic upheaval.

The temperature on the face of the photosphere averages 10,000° F. This is 2,500 times cooler than the center of the sun, but it is still so hot that only 18 kinds of molecules, or combinations of atoms, can hold together long enough for their identifying spectral lines to be observed from the earth. Even atoms have trouble holding together: most of them are ionized—their normal, neutral balance of electrical charges lost—most of the time. The electrons that escape fly about freely, building up electric winds and storms; positively charged atomic nuclei roam almost equally free.

Under the circumstances, it is not surprising that the surface of the sun is usually pock-marked with magnetic bumps and eddies. The principal eruptions are sunspots, appearing as dark "holes" in the bright white skin 500 to 50,000 or more miles wide. Mysteriously growing more numerous every 11 years, sunspots seem to be part of a 22-year cycle in which the entire magnetic field of the sun may reverse itself, the north magnetic pole becoming a south pole and the south a north. The last reversal took place in 1957-1958, when sunspot activity was at a maximum. During this period, the north geographic pole of the sun became a weak magnetic south pole. The zone of sunspot activity drifted toward the solar equator, and by late 1964 a minimum number of sunspots were observed. Then, starting a new cycle, spots began to appear about 30° from the equator. This active zone increased as it moved into lower latitudes, to reach a climax in 1968 and 1969.

During their brief lives—three to four months at most—sunspots often seem to travel in pairs, one in front and one behind. In the sun's northern hemisphere the spots that travel in front are polarized the same way as the north pole is at the time. The ones that trail along behind show the opposite polarity. In the sun's southern hemisphere the situation is reversed.

According to current theories, sunspots may be regions where huge hoops, following magnetic lines of force inside the sun, break through the photosphere and complete their circuits through the thin solar atmosphere beyond. Arches of extra-bright gas often are seen in the sun's atmosphere above a pair of sunspots. Sometimes these arches, called prominences, reach a height of 30,000

The Marvelous Secrets of Light

A CONTINUOUS SPECTRUM is formed when light from a hot solid or a dense gas is passed through a slit and shone through a triangular wedge of glass known as a prism. This "white light," as it is called by scientists, contains every color. The prism separates these colors into the familiar rainbow.

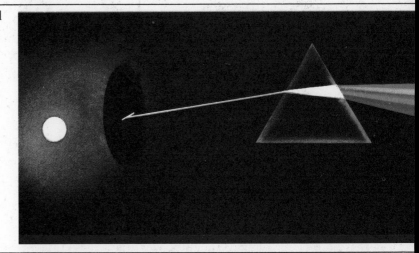

A BRIGHT-LINE SPECTRUM, or emission spectrum, is produced by glowing gases of low density, such as those found in space. Unlike the continuous spectrum, this one is broken into narrow lines of color; these can be used to identify the chemicals in the gas, like a set of fingerprints.

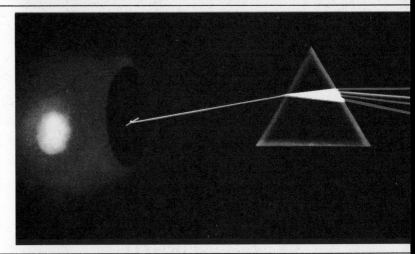

A DARK-LINE SPECTRUM, or absorption spectrum, results when light from a hot glowing body passes through a cooler gas. The gas absorbs light in the parts of the spectrum where it can emit bright lines (above). The resulting gaps, seen as black lines, are used to determine what the gas is made of.

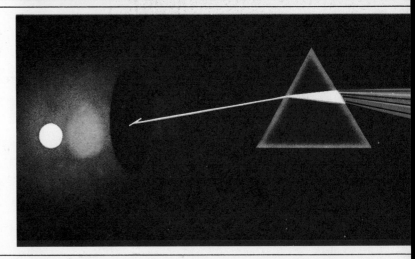

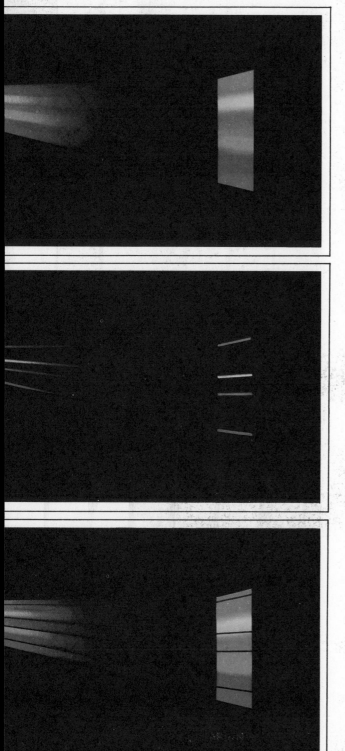

miles and span more than 125,000 miles.

Hoops that have quietly arched across thousands of miles for days may abruptly explode, shooting atoms out into space at speeds above the escape velocity—384 miles per second—imposed by the sun's gravitational field. Other magnetic discharges create tornadoes and leaping tongues of fiery hydrogen that shoot up 100,000 miles or more above the sun's surface. The greatest events of all, however, are not these prominences but flares—outbursts of glowing gas hugging the surface near the sunspots—which propel invisible spurts of ionized gas, or "plasma," all the way to the earth and beyond. Here the plasma clouds interact with our upper atmosphere; they black out short-wave radio transmission and create the shimmering polar auroras we know as the Northern Lights.

Immediately after leaving the sun, these solar eruptions pass through the corona, the sun's outer sheath. Beyond the corona, a further mist of matter may extend invisibly out to the farthest frontiers of the solar system. But the corona extends barely to Mercury, and the part of it that can actually be seen is much smaller, reaching at most one sixth as far. This visible portion can be seen during eclipses—or even in full daylight, thanks to a device invented in 1930 by the French astronomer Bernard Lyot. With Lyot's "coronagraph," which creates an artificial eclipse by masking the

(*Text continued on page 77*)

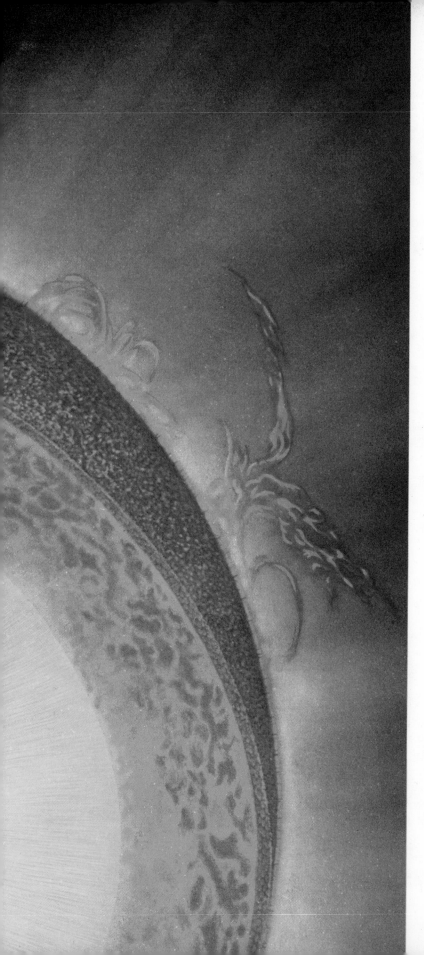

The Solar Furnace

The sun's power plant, seen in this cutaway drawing, is its white-hot inner core, where hydrogen fuses into helium at 25 million degrees F. Energy, released in violent gamma rays, pours toward the surface 300,000 miles away. The rays smash through a 200,000 mile zone *(yellow)*, where they collide with densely packed gas atoms and lose enough energy to turn into X-rays and ultraviolet rays. The surface of the 200-mile-thick photosphere is marked by sunspots *(far left)* that look dark against its brilliance. The 4,000-mile-deep chromosphere—the sun's dense lower atmosphere—flings up gas in displays such as the arch and the jetlike feature at upper left. The outer atmosphere, the corona, reaches as far as Mercury, 36 million miles away, but it is only bright enough for observation near the sun.

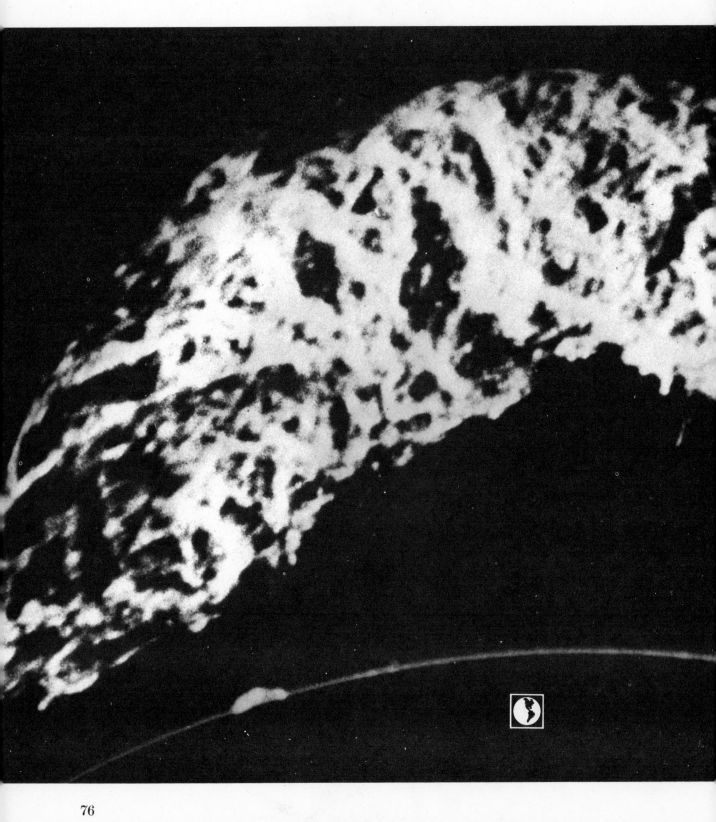

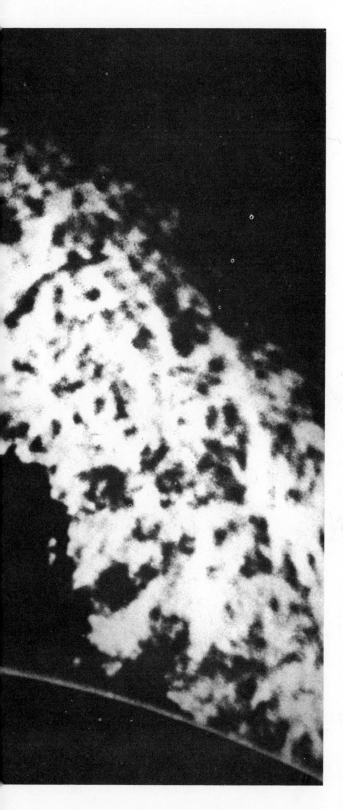

main light of the sun, the corona appears as a faint, nebulous light flaring outward from the sun's hidden hub.

All of the radiant energy and the matter blown away in the solar wind represents a total loss. Therefore, it is clear that from the moment the sun first began to blaze it has been spending its energy and growing old. Astronomers today pretty much agree on how the sun was born and on how it will ultimately die.

According to theory, the sun came into being about five billion years ago—at least five billion years after the formation of the Milky Way galaxy. The gas out of which the sun condensed was almost all hydrogen, dark and full of swirls and eddies. This gas probably began to condense when enough atoms happened to swirl together so that their combined gravity bound them into a single collapsing cloud. Very slowly the matter of the cloud began to clump around the densest eddies of gas. By far the largest of these clumps was the protosun, the mass of gas that would condense to become the sun. Its powerful gravitation shaped the rest of the cloud into a huge, rotating disk.

Million-Mile Fireworks

An eruptive arch, among the most dramatic solar spectacles, soars above the seething surface of the sun. One of the largest explosions of its kind ever recorded, it was photographed in June 1946, when it was about one hour old. This flamelike display remained visible for more than two hours and stretched nearly a million miles into space.

Sunspots and Solar Storms

Churning across the surface of the sun, sunspots appear to be giant magnetic storms. They are much darker than other areas of the sun (*see closeup below*) because they are much cooler—they are a mere 8,400° F., while the rest of the surface is 10,000°. The red-light photograph at right is of a solar storm region in action. If the large ridge at upper right were viewed from the side, it would look like the huge fiery arch on the previous page.

Within the disk the helter-skelter movements of atoms and molecules became more orderly as they collided, and the heat of the collisions radiated off into space. In this way, the energy of the cloud's internal motions was reduced and the particles were reined in until most of them whirled in orderly fashion around the protosun or around the lesser eddies in the cloud. These lesser eddies, rolling lazily around on one another like ball bearings, were the protoplanets. As they too began to contract around their central eddies, the heavy substances in them tended to condense first and to cluster toward their centers.

In the meantime, the jostling crush of atoms falling into the protosun was creating heat inside it—heat that gathered more quickly than it could be shed. The temperature in the protosun's core rose steadily. As the core's temperature passed the million-degree mark, thermonuclear reactions began adding energy to the heat already being released. The sun's surface turned slowly red and hot, orange and hotter, yellow and incandescent. Its first rays, falling on the half-formed planets, began to drive away the stardust on which they were still feeding. Soon the protoplanets became distinguishable in their separate orbits and

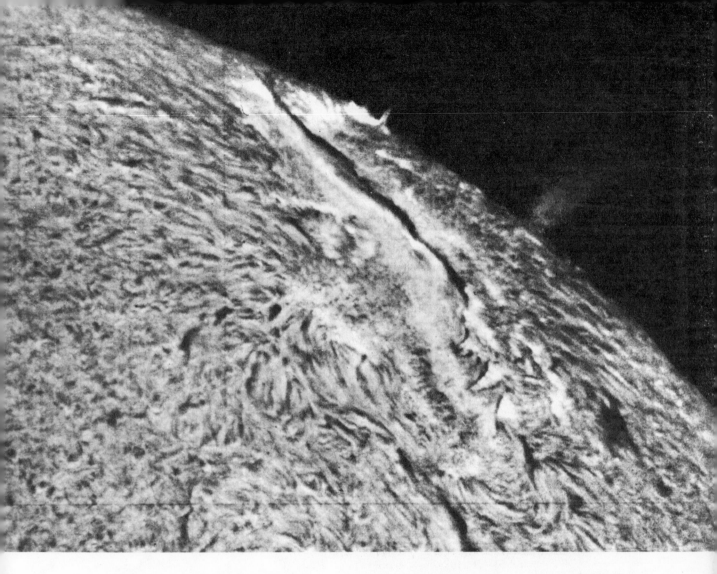

began to condense into their present form.

At the sun's first dawn, several of the protoplanets had not yet collected all the solid matter in their spheres of influence. As the sun's new radiation blew away the outer layers of the protoplanets, these bodies lost the gravitational power needed to pull in their outriding fragments. These leftover subplanets either became permanent satellites or drifted away as independent bodies.

The first light of the sun was very dim because the sun was still contracting and the fuel in its core was less tightly packed than it is now. Once the sun stopped contracting —after approximately one million years— the solar energy rose to within 20 per cent of its present value, driving off the original cloud and leaving the planets to work out their further evolution alone. Since then, some asteroids have been swallowed by collisions with the earth, the moon and the other planets and satellites. But by and large the solar system has probably remained much the way it was created. The sun's family, however, cannot remain unchanged forever, because the sun must itself start to change again as it burns its hydrogen fuel and begins to die.

The future evolution of the sun has also

The Birth of the Solar System

Scientists believe that the solar system began as a cloud of gas (*top left*) which gradually became more compact and began rotating (*top right*). A large lump of gas collected in the middle (*center left*), and began glowing as smaller lumps formed and circled it (*center right*). The center lump became the sun and the outer lumps shrank and hardened into planets (*bottom left*). Finally a solar system emerged (*bottom right*), shown in this simplified diagram with only four planets.

80

been worked out by astronomers. If it were to continue spending its entire hydrogen content at its present rate—only 657 tons of hydrogen each second—it would go on burning for another 50 billion years or more. But long before that, rising temperature caused by the sheer weight of ash in its core will ignite other nuclear processes, and the sun will start burning its fuel much faster than it does now. About five billion years from now the speed-up will begin and the sun will start swelling; its output of energy will increase. In another billion years the average temperature on earth will rise to something like 1,000° F., the oceans will boil away and lead will melt like molasses. In the words of

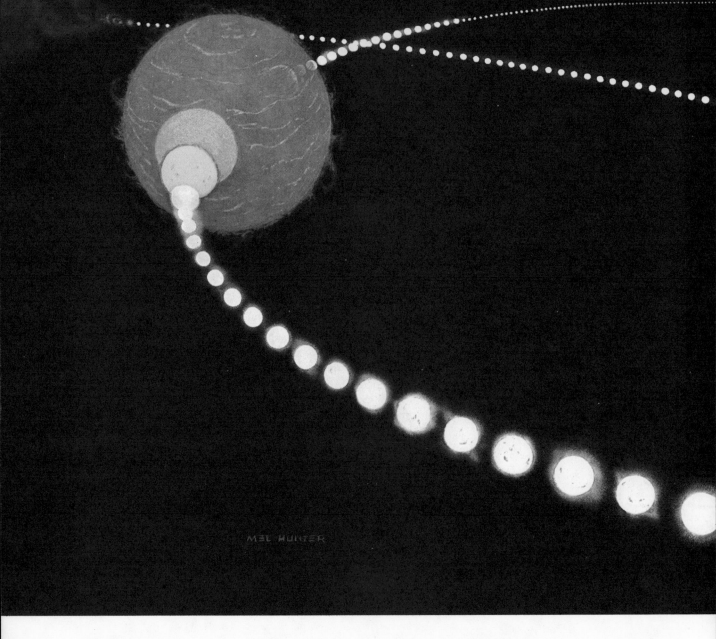

Palomar's Allan Sandage, "Conditions will be miserable."

Later the sun will shrink again, perhaps undergoing instabilities and eruptions as it does so. In its last long death throes, it will continue to shrink while the fires inside it go out and the only glow it emits is energy from the gravitational squeeze of its spent, collapsing matter. Little by little it will dwindle until it is smaller than the earth, its gases so densely packed that a bucketful of them would weigh more than a battleship. For hundreds of billions of years more, the sun will continue to cool, giving off only infrared rays. Then it will go out completely, black and cold as the most remote regions of space around it. Astronomers can foretell how the sun will die, simply by looking around at other stars and seeing what is happening to them.

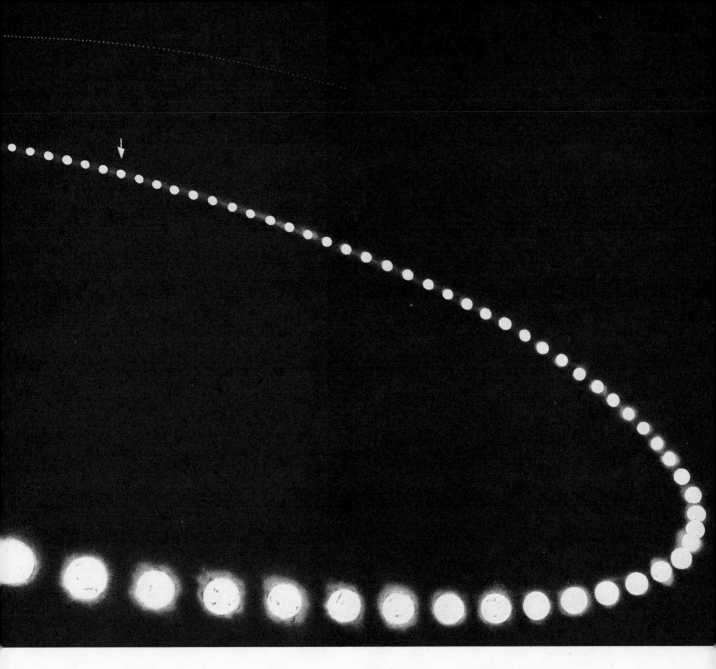

The Sun from Birth to Death

Born from a cloud of gas *(top left)* five billion years ago, the sun is now at the point indicated by the arrow in this painting. Five billion years from now it is expected to expand to a "red giant" *(left)*, frying its nearby planets before fading into a black "dwarf" as cold as the space around it.

5

What Our Galaxy Is Made Of

Except for the golden face of the nearby sun, we see every star in the sky as a fine point of twinkling light. If the earth had no atmosphere, and the space around it were quite empty, our largest telescope would barely show the largest nearby stars as tiny circular dots. But the earth's shimmering layers of air mask the stars' images, making each one a twinkling blur. Whether they look bright as bombs or dim as fireflies, telescopes show them only as fuzzy points of light without dimensions.

Man has long wondered exactly what and where the stars are. Only in the last few decades has he learned the answers to these questions. The stars, like the sun, are vast thermonuclear reactors, arranged in huge systems called galaxies. The sun and all of the other 7,000-odd stars that can be seen by the unaided eye are simply a few

A GALAXY'S ANATOMY, much like that of our own Milky Way, is shown in a photograph of the galaxy in the constellation Andromeda. Its spiral arms are blue with the light of young stars. Overexposed here, its hub looks white, but it actually consists of old red stars like those seen around it.

What the Milky Way Really Looks Like

These two illustrations give a good picture of the solar system's neighborhood. Since the solar system is far from the center of the Milky Way, we see most of our galaxy as a band of hazy white across the sky. In the photograph above, however, special film sensitive to light that penetrates the hazy gases has been used to show the galaxy's hub (the three black bands are braces supporting the film holder). If we could view the Milky Way from a distance we would see it as a lens-shaped disk (*below*). The two crosses in the drawing indicate the galaxy's center and the location of the sun.

members of one galaxy, the Milky Way.

In finding out how the stars are arranged in space, astronomers have studied more than a million stars and recorded their positions. But to see the universe in three dimensions they also needed to know the distances to the stars as well. The most direct way to measure a star's distance is by its parallax, determined by the amount its position seems to change against the background of more distant stars. But this method is less and less accurate as the distance increases; 500 light-years is considered its limit.

Before 1838, when a star's parallax was first measured, astronomers thought that all stars probably were equally bright, and that some appeared dimmer than others only because they were farther away. They carefully measured the visible brightness—the "magnitude"—of stars, hoping to translate these figures into distances by the simple formula: brighter for closer, fainter for farther. But when astronomers found by parallax the distances to nearby stars, they realized at once that faintness and brightness do not depend on distance alone —some stars actually are much brighter than others. To the naked eye, for instance, the two brightest stars in the sky are Sirius (in the constellation of Canis Majoris, the Great Dog) and Canopus (in the constellation Carina, the Keel). Sirius seems twice as bright as Canopus, but it turns out from their parallaxes that Sirius is only 8.7 light-years away, while Canopus is 100 light-years away. Canopus actually is not fainter than Sirius, but 65 times brighter.

Even though this brightness comparison would not work for stars in general, astronomers still hoped that it might work among stars of any one kind. To see if it would, they first had to classify the stars near the sun, find their distances by parallax and then find distant duplicates of each kind of star. Altogether, many star types have been discovered that do reveal their distances according to the simple formula of brighter-nearer, fainter-farther. One of the most important types—because it can be seen the farthest—is the "Cepheid variable," a pulsating star that grows brighter and dimmer in regular periods as it radiates hotter and cooler. The longer a Cepheid takes to run through its cycle of change, the greater is its average true brightness. A Cepheid that grows faint and bright and faint again over a period of 30 days has an average brightness 4,000 times that of the sun. A Cepheid with a one-day period averages only 100 times as bright as the sun. After measuring the pulsation period of a Cepheid, astronomers can calculate its average true brightness, or absolute magnitude, with 90 per cent accuracy. By comparing the result with the star's average visible brightness, or apparent magnitude, they can work out its distance. And they are able to do this whether the star is only 650 light-years away, like Polaris, the nearest Cepheid, or over two million light-years away,

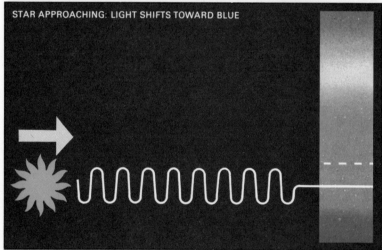

STAR STATIONARY: LIGHT SEEN IN TRUE COLOR

STAR APPROACHING: LIGHT SHIFTS TOWARD BLUE

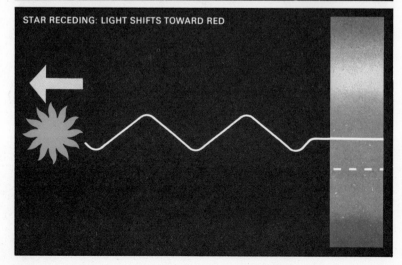

STAR RECEDING: LIGHT SHIFTS TOWARD RED

The Doppler Effect

Astronomers use a phenomenon called the "Doppler effect" to determine whether a star is moving toward or away from the earth. If a star is standing still relative to the earth, the light it gives off will be seen in its "true" color or place in the spectrum *(top)*. But if the star is moving toward the earth, the waves of its light will "pile up" in front of it, making each wave length seem shorter, or bluer, than it really is *(center)*. The same principle makes a racing car's engine appear to emit a higher whine, or shorter wave lengths of sound, as it approaches you *(below right)*. If the star is moving away, the wave lengths are stretched out and shift toward the red end of the spectrum *(bottom)*—just as the sound waves from the racing car's engine are stretched out, the sound descending to a low roar as the car passes you and moves away.

such as those in the Andromeda galaxy.

Most of the other kinds of stars that serve as distance gauges are not so easily recognizable as Cepheids, but they can be used to measure the nearer regions where Cepheids are scarce. In the middle distance of the Milky Way, astronomers often take advantage of "RR Lyrae" stars, a pulsating species that grows bright and dim more rapidly and faintly than Cepheids. The specific true brightness of still other stars can be identified by their spectral lines and the color of their light.

Astronomers knew that all the stars they could see were in motion long before they knew that these stars were all whirling around the center of the Milky Way. They called simple star movements across the sky "proper motions" and measured them by small, progressive shifts in the position of a star on a sky map. For some nearby stars it took only a few years to work out proper motions, but it has taken centuries to calculate them for more distant stars.

Besides proper motions, 19th Century astronomers measured "radial velocities," the motions of stars toward or away from the sun. As it travels through space, a star moves forward into its own light waves, pushing the wave crests closer together than they would be normally. Similarly, the light waves behind it are slightly pulled apart by its motion away from them. As a result the light waves in front of a moving star become shorter in length and higher in frequency, therefore seeming bluer. Behind a moving star the waves are longer in wave length, lower in frequency and redder. This change is known as the "Doppler shift," and it is measured by the way emission and absorption lines shift their positions on the spectrum in amounts that depend exactly on the speed of a star toward or away from the earth.

Combined, this information forms our picture of the Milky Way, the great, dy-

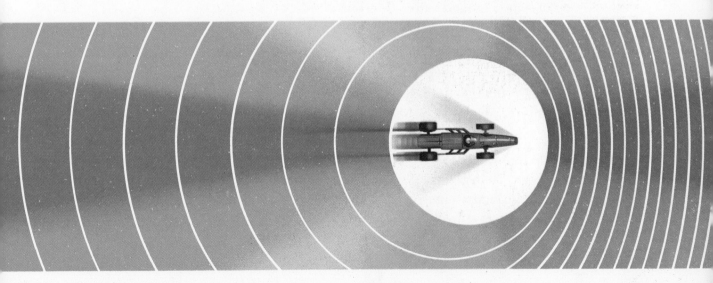

namic system in which our sun is just one of 100 billion stars. From our position in the wheel of the Milky Way, we can glimpse only its nearby portions, which form a band of stars across the skies of both hemispheres. The fact that the Milky Way is a single spiral galaxy, turning slowly in the immensity of space, only became clear after the discovery of other galaxies in all directions as far as modern telescopes can see.

The Milky Way is thickest over the Southern Hemisphere where, beyond the constellation Sagittarius, lies our galaxy's hub—a flattened globe 10,000 to 15,000 light-years thick, packed with gigantic red stars, veiled in clouds of dust and "visible" to us mainly in infrared and radio waves. Outside of the hub and revolving around it is a disk of stars, gas and dust 80,000 light-years in diameter. Inside of the disk, arms of dark dust and gas, spangled with countless brilliant blue stars, spiral outward from the hub like showers of sparks around a fireworks pin wheel. Many bright stars in the hub are red, the bright stars in the arms are blue, but the star that we know best, the sun, is neither. As only a fifth-magnitude star, up to 100,000 times fainter than its brightest neighbors, the sun shines with a mild yellow light. It is 30,000 light-years, or three quarters of the way, from the center of the hub, and orbits around it once every 250 million years.

The sun and all the other stars in the disk of the Milky Way compose only one of the galaxy's two main star populations. For all its vastness, the disk is roughly comparable to the disk of planets around the sun. But the Milky Way also has a much larger part: a dustless, spherical halo of stars and star clusters 100,000 light-years in diameter—similar to the distant sphere of comets around the sun and the planets. Many halo stars are red and very old.

The star clusters of the halo are almost miniature galaxies in their own right, each tightly packed with tens of thousands of bright stars. Since they are shaped like balls or globes, they are called "globular" clusters. The halo also has several billion individual stars traveling alone, like our runaway comets, on wildly tilted orbits. A few of them have actually penetrated the disk in the regions near the sun. They seem to move faster than disk stars because they do not travel in the same direction as the sun, but swoop by the disk from one side or the other at 50 to 200 miles a second.

While discovering where the stars are and how they move, scientists also found out that stars can be very different from each other. One important difference among them is the speed at which they spin. At their equators, most small stars like the sun move at only one or two miles per second, but many of the massive stars spin as fast as 200 miles per second. An example of a fast-spinning star is Pleione, a member of the Pleiades cluster. Pleione's equator rotates at 190 miles per second, so fast that it hurls gas off into space, ringing its waist with matter that glows as it reacts to Pleione's intense ultraviolet rays.

Other major differences among stars are indicated by temperature and brightness. Taking a star's temperature can be done by finding in what section of the spectrum it shines most brightly. In general, if it is brightest in red light, it is a "cool" star; if it is brightest in yellow light, it is a "warm" star; if it is brightest in blue light, it is a "hot" star. The total brightness of a star can be measured by adding up the intensities of its light at many wave lengths.

One of the most important things to know about a star is its mass. From a star's mass, the amount of matter in it, scientists can work out what all its other properties should be after it has been shining for any given time. They can also tell a star's age from the way it is shining, if they know its mass. Unfortunately, a star's mass is often the hardest thing to find out about it.

A star's mass can be figured out directly only if it is a "double star," a pair of stars that look to the naked eye like one star but are actually two circling each other. The orbits of double, or binary, stars are controlled by their mutual gravitational fields. From the amount of time two such stars take to revolve around each other, and from the distance between them, their masses can be deduced. Fortunately, 75 per cent of the stars do have one or more companions with which they dance as they follow their orbits around the Milky Way.

Antares in the constellation Scorpio, the 16th most brilliant star in the sky, is really two stars. Capella and Alpha Centauri are each three; Castor is really six stars.

The first double star ever seen was Mizar, at the bend of the Big Dipper's handle, which the improved telescopes of 1650 showed as two stars where only one had been seen before. In 1889 the brighter one of Mizar's stars was in turn subdivided by the spectroscope, which split its light into two separate rainbows alternately overlapping each other, indicating that Mizar was really three stars. The number of stars with several components made visible by the telescope has since been increased by an even larger number revealed by the spectroscope.

Of all the strange multiple stars only the double stars reveal their masses, because the motions of three-star, four-star and many-star groups are often too complicated even for modern mathematics. However, there are enough double stars, or binaries, to show astronomers how much matter there is in stars in general. From each item of such knowledge flows a great deal of other knowledge. For instance, the star called UW Canis Majoris is a double star with a total mass 36 times that of the sun. From this, and the fact that this UW pair is 10,000 times as bright as the sun, scientists can calculate that the pair will burn out and die in 300,-000 years. Astronomers have now sorted out the many kinds of stars in the Milky Way by mass, brightness, temperature, composi-

A Dark Horse of Star Dust

The Horsehead Nebula, a cloud of cool gas and star
dust in the Milky Way near the east end of Orion's
belt, rears against a background of gas glowing with
energy from nearby stars. Such nebulae are really
thin cosmic mists but sometimes are banked so deep
they completely hide the stars behind them.

tion, spin and magnetic strength, and have arranged them in two main groups: "normal" stars and "abnormal" stars.

Normal stars are in the majority, and they burn the way astrophysicists expect stars to burn. From the principles of nuclear fusion, scientists can calculate how stars made of hydrogen ought to shine. Massive stars, in which gravity jams the fuel most quickly and strongly toward the center, should burn far more rapidly and generate far more energy than lightweight stars, in which the central fuel is loosely packed. In terms of what can be seen, big stars are brightly blue and hot, while medium-sized stars are moderately warm and yellow and small stars dimly cool and red.

This sequence of brightness and color among normal stars is arranged by spectral types in an order using the letters O, B, A, F, G, K and M (a classification students still remember with help from the sentence, "Oh, Be a Fine Girl: Kiss Me"). Each type represents a range of color and temperature. Massive, brilliant O-stars at one end of the spectrum are hot and blue and range from 90,000° F. down to 45,000° F. in surface temperature. They are so hot that most of their energy is emitted in ultraviolet rays. Light, dim M-stars are cool and red and range from 6,000° F. to 3,000° F. They emit most of their energy in infrared heat rays. Middleweight, yellow G-stars, like the sun, fall at the center of the spectrum. Their surface temperatures range from 10,000° F. to 9,000° F. and almost all their energy is emit-

ted in the visible fraction of the spectrum.

Most "abnormal" stars are overbright for their spectral type. At one end of the spectrum there are overbright blue "supergiants," such as Rigel, in Orion. Although Rigel is 900 light-years away from the earth it appears as the seventh brightest star in the sky because it pours out 60,000 times the energy the sun does. The opposite end of the spectrum includes red giants such as Arcturus, in Boötes, the fourth brightest star, and red supergiants such as Betelgeuse, in Orion, the ninth brightest star. Between these extremes there are white, yellow and orange giants and supergiants—and a variety of pulsating and exploding stars: orange and yellow Cepheids, white RR Lyrae stars and exploding stars of billion-sun brightness called supernovae.

As well as overbright abnormal stars, there are also underbright ones. Erupting stars called novae are usually dim for their color but grow overbright when they flare up. Extremely underbright stars are called "white dwarfs." Each of these dwarfs contains about as much matter as the sun, but it is densely packed into volumes the size of the planet Mercury and weighs from one to 20 or more tons per cubic inch. Probably the matter in white dwarfs has all been converted into nuclear ash—atoms incapable of any more reactions.

White dwarfs seem to be dying, and most other abnormal stars are actively unstable, or show signs of future instability. For these reasons astronomers conclude that abnormal stars are old and dying. But such stars are a tiny minority of all stars. For every ultraviolet Rigel, 30 times as massive, 50,000 times as bright and probably 100,000 times as short-lived as the sun, there exist 200,000 yellow suns and several million faint red M-stars smaller than the sun.

A typical sample of the Milky Way's star population lies within 16 light-years of the sun. It includes 50 stars: 28 singles, eight doubles and two triples. In addition there are five invisible companions, which can only be detected by their effect on the motions of their visible partners. Of these 50 nearby stars, four are burned-out white dwarfs; two are fast-burning bright white A-stars; one is a brilliant yellow-white F-star; two are mild yellow G-stars like the sun; seven are small orange K-stars; and 34 are tiny red M-stars.

This sample clearly shows the sun to be a comparatively big frog in its own pond. But the little red stars form a solid majority, and their great advantage is that, as slow-burners, they will remain shining billions of years after the sun has gone out.

A Breeding Ground for Stars

The telescope shows Theta Orionis, the sparkling middle "star" in the sword of the constellation Orion, to be much more than a star. It is a gaseous cloud bright with radiation from four hot stars within it. Astronomers hope, by observing it, to find out if stars are born in gas clouds like this.

6
The Birth, Life and Death of Stars

A GIANT AMONG TELESCOPES, atop Mount Palomar in California, dwarfs the man underneath it. The openwork tube that holds the 200-inch mirror weighs 125 tons and the yoke that supports it weighs 300 tons. Yet the entire instrument is so delicately balanced that one hand can turn it.

In discovering where and what the stars are, astronomers found clues to their origin and development, or "stellar evolution." The many kinds of stars are ranged in orderly sequences of development. Even most "abnormal" stars prove to be simply stages in the lives of normal stars. Now astronomers can describe the birth, lifetime and death of most stars, and even roughly estimate the time when the stars of the Milky Way must all fade and die.

The credit for this great accomplishment belongs to hundreds of scientists. One pioneer, the English astronomer Sir Arthur Stanley Eddington, first realized the importance of mass in a star's life. He saw that once a star is formed with a certain amount of matter in it, the rest of its life is determined by a constant tug of war between two opposite forces. While its own gravitation draws it together, the energy from its nuclear furnace provides an outward force that tends to push it apart. Another pioneer was Palomar's Walter Baade, who realized that the different kinds of stars shining in a given group revealed much about the entire group's age and

A Tiny, Man-made "Star"

The world's first hydrogen-fusion blast, in 1952, was caused by the same nuclear process as the one that powers the sun and many other stars. Less than a century ago no one knew how these stellar furnaces worked. Now man not only understands them, but can even duplicate them in miniature.

about the development of individual stars in it. Baade compared just two populations: the halo stars in the spheres around galaxies and the disk stars that form the bulk of spiral galaxies like the Milky Way.

Baade found that halo stars are mostly reddish, and that halos lack the dust and gas needed to form new stars. He deduced that halo stars are an old population whose massive, fast-burning blue stars have already died. The survivors are mainly small, normal yellow and red stars. The few red giants among them are beginning to die.

In contrast to the halo, a galaxy's disk is rich in raw material for new stars. Most of this star stuff is in the swirling gas and dust of the disk's spiral arms. Baade noted that stars in the spiral arms are usually much more blue and brilliant—much more massive and fast-burning—than stars elsewhere in a galaxy. He concluded that they are new stars and that disk stars include a mixed, relatively young population, with fresh stars of all sizes continually forming from gas and dust clouds. Disk stars are of all types and ages: new blue massive stars, new to middle-aged middleweight stars, and new to old lightweight stars.

A star's birth is always similar to the birth of the sun, already described in Chapter 4. A cloud of dust and gas whirls into pockets of high density and then begins to contract around one or more of its gravitational centers. Many centers in one tight cloud can result in a single star plus planets, a multiple star, or a multiple star plus planets. The final result depends on the density and size of the original cloud and how rough-and-tumble its movements are. Astronomers think they may see protostars in the very act of contracting in the nearby clouds of the Milky Way's spiral arms.

When a protostar contracts, its central regions are warmed by the release of gravitational energy—the heat caused as atoms drawn to the core become so crowded that they collide. When the core has grown hot enough, its hydrogen begins to fuse into helium. At first the fusions of single atoms are rare, and release little energy. But, as more matter gathers in the star's outer layers, their weight increases and presses the atoms in the core closer together so that they collide and fuse more and more often. Eventually these fusions produce exactly enough energy for pressure from the heated gases to counteract the star's inpulling gravitation. At that point the star has arrived at a stable, mature state. If the star is very massive, its strong gravitation has made it condense fast, and its highly compressed, hot core pours out huge amounts of fusion energy to stave off further crushing and collapse. However, if the star is a slight one, it has contracted gradually and gently. The occasional fusion of its uncrowded inner atoms gives off only enough energy to offset its weak gravitation.

The balance between gravity and fusion turns any star into a normal star and it remains one for most of its life. But once it has consumed about 10 per cent of the hydrogen fuel in its central core, it begins to grow overbright. This happens in a few hundred thousand years with hot, blue, massive, fast-burning stars; in a few billion years with mild, yellow, sun-sized, temperately burning stars; or in a few hundred billion years with cool, red, light, slow-burning stars. The sun is expected to reach this point in another three to five billion years.

A star begins to brighten thus when enough helium ash has gathered in its core. As the ash piles up in the center, fusion continues in a bright skin around this core. The ash contracts under its own growing weight, squeezing its atomic nuclei together. This energy raises the temperature of the core and the extra heat speeds up the fusion reactions in the skin around it.

Set off by this increasing inner radiation, the gas in the star's outer regions grows hotter and begins to boil and swell; the star grows brighter. But now its outer layer is so far from the nuclear furnaces inside that the surface slowly cools; the cool, puffed-up star looks red. If it is many times more massive than the sun, it becomes a red supergiant like Betelgeuse in the constellation Orion. If it is sun-sized or only a little more massive, it becomes a slightly swollen red or orange giant. Stars less massive than the sun will undoubtedly follow this pattern, but there is no known example because lightweight, slow-burning stars have not

had time since the formation of the Milky Way to reach this point.

In its overbright state a star burns its hydrogen at a dizzying pace, and helium ash piles up in its core more and more rapidly. This added ash increases the gravitational squeeze and raises the temperature in the core. The rising heat in turn steps up the rate both of fusion and of ash production.

After 40 per cent of the hydrogen in the core of a sun-sized star has been burned, the core contracts, producing temperatures of some 200 million degrees F.—hot enough for the helium ash to become active fuel. Helium atoms then can merge explosively to form carbon, oxygen and neon. All these nuclear reactions throw off gamma-ray energy, changing the star's core from evenly heated, inactive gas into active, vibrant gas, hotter at its center—where the new reactions are—than at the skin of its core, where hydrogen is still fusing.

At this point a star's core explodes in what is known as the helium flash, or "popping of the core." Astronomers think this violent "pop" almost rips a star apart, but the thick outer blanket of gases absorbs the shock, and the blast just spreads the core matter into the layers around. The star grows abruptly hotter, bluer and smaller.

Being heavier than hydrogen, the ash elements distributed throughout the star by the first explosion probably sink toward its center again and form a new core. But this time the core is two-ply, the central ball

Y CYGNI	RIGEL
SPICA	REGULUS
SIRIUS	VEGA
ALTAIR	DENEB
CASTOR	CANOPUS
PROCYON	THE SUN
ALPHA CENTAURI	CAPELLA
POLARIS	ARCTURUS
ALDEBARAN	POLLUX
BETELGEUSE	ANTARES

Color and Energy in Stars

Although most stars look whitish to the naked eye, they really are of various colors. This chart, which includes most of the brightest visible stars, starts in the top lefthand corner with Y Cygni (in the constellation Cygnus, the Swan), a blue star that spends much of its power in ultraviolet rays. The others range down, from left to right, through blue-white, white, yellow-white, yellow and orange to the warm red stars at the bottom, which send out much of their energy in heat waves.

formed mainly of oxygen, carbon and neon, with helium composing most of the next shell outward. Outside the helium there is a layer of fusing hydrogen. The star is now burning on two levels at the same time: one where hydrogen is becoming helium, and another inside it where helium is becoming oxygen, carbon and neon.

If the star is massive enough, it may create so much gravitational heat that the neon core "pops" just as the helium core did. At about 1.4 billion degrees F. neon ash starts fusing, producing still heavier magnesium ash. At about 2.7 billion degrees such elements as aluminum, silicon and sul-phur begin to form. At nearly four billion degrees these elements in turn are transmuted into still heavier ones, such as iron, nickel and zinc. In a very massive star a series of reactions could take place at the same time, the ash from each one becoming fuel for a hotter one inside it.

When a star pops its core it soon consumes the rest of its nuclear energy, then its gravitational pressure compresses it until the atomic nuclei resist further contraction. After that, the star, now a white dwarf, simply cools off for billions of years.

Extremely massive stars must shed their excess matter before they can die. Most of

these rare massive stars spin fast and they probably can simply hurl off matter from their whirling equators. A certain number of massive stars, however, are born spinning slowly and their deaths are among the most dramatic sights in the entire heavens.

When the helium flash occurs in a massive slow-spinning star, the explosion is likely to be cushioned by the star's gravity. This is probably true of all the heavier inner layers that develop in succession later. Eventually a slow-spinner may burn on seven separate layers, like the skins of an onion, going from light hydrogen on the outside to heavy iron in the deep interior.

Young Stars and Old Stars

When scientists discovered that the age of stars could be determined by their color and brightness, they also discovered that, like people, stars of a certain age are often found together. The stars in the group known as the Pleiades (*far left*) burn with the bright, blue-white color of younger stars. The stars above, which belong to a cluster called Messier 3, are the weak yellow of older stars.

The nuclear reaction that creates iron releases vast amounts of energy. As the star shrinks to fill in for this loss, the core temperature rockets in a matter of weeks. At about 12 billion degrees the build-up from light to heavy elements is suddenly reversed. Iron and the others break down into helium and in so doing absorb energy instead of releasing it. Without the outward push of energy to balance its gravitation, the star collapses like a pricked balloon. In a moment, all the remaining nuclear energy in the star is released at once, hurling out almost as much light as an entire galaxy in a final splash as brilliant as hundreds of millions of stars.

Stars of this type are so scarce that their explosions are as rare as they are spectacular. Modern astronomers label them "supernovae" and have seen them only in distant galaxies. In the Milky Way the last supernova was seen in 1604 A.D., the next-to-last in 1572 A.D.

Small stellar explosions—thousands of times weaker and more common than supernovae—are known as "novae," short for *novae stellae*, or "new stars." They were named long before they were understood; to the early sky-watchers who saw stars blazing up where they had seen nothing before, the name was perfectly natural.

OXYGEN

HIGH-SPEED ELECTRONS, NITROGEN, OTHER ELEMENTS

NITROGEN AND HYDROGEN

HIGH-SPEED ELECTRONS

In spite of all scientists know about the life of the stars themselves, they have found no sign of biological life around other stars. There is no reason why most stars should not have planets born from the same gas clouds as the star, as the sun's planets were. Since most stars have habitable zones around them where water can be water, where gas can be held as atmosphere, and radiation can be received in warming wave lengths, astronomers do not doubt that life should have evolved around millions of the 100 billion stars in the Milky Way.

One might expect that intelligent beings on such planets would try to communicate with other inhabitants of their galaxy. It is

The Debris of a Superstar

A vast, greenish cloud of expanding gases called the Crab Nebula (*far left*) is all that remains of a huge, exploding star, or supernova. Ancient oriental observers saw the explosion in 1054 A.D., but the event was forgotten. Not until the 18th Century did astronomers realize that the swirling gases were the remains of a star. Modern astronomers have analyzed the formation by photographing it with special film and color filters. The pictures above show some of the components of the mighty cloud today.

possible that some of them are trying. Radio astronomers listen periodically for signals from other worlds, with no result, as yet. But it is very unlikely that anyone will stumble on the direction and frequency of such an interstellar radio station before centuries of hit-or-miss effort.

The need to communicate with the creatures of other suns may seem small, but a surprising number of scientists feel that man may have to make contact with them and share technological knowledge if the human race is to live to a ripe old age. Many faint, cool M-stars near the sun have life expectancies over a hundred billion years longer than the sun's. On the planets of such stars, if anywhere, the human race may be able to enjoy the full fruits of biological and cultural evolution.

But eventually even the smallest, most slowly burning stars will die. Finally the gas clouds must give out, and the Milky Way will contain no new stars at all. For a long time the fading galaxy will send out a little heat as its white dwarfs cool off. Then the last white dwarfs will grow as dark and cold as the space beyond the Milky Way.

A Glowing "Bubble" of Gas

The Dumb-Bell nebula, named for its shape, is a rare kind of cosmic cloud. The blue-white star at its center has hurled off a sphere of gas, as if blowing a huge soap bubble around itself. The star emits ultraviolet rays, which cause the gassy sphere to shine in fluorescent shades of red and blue.

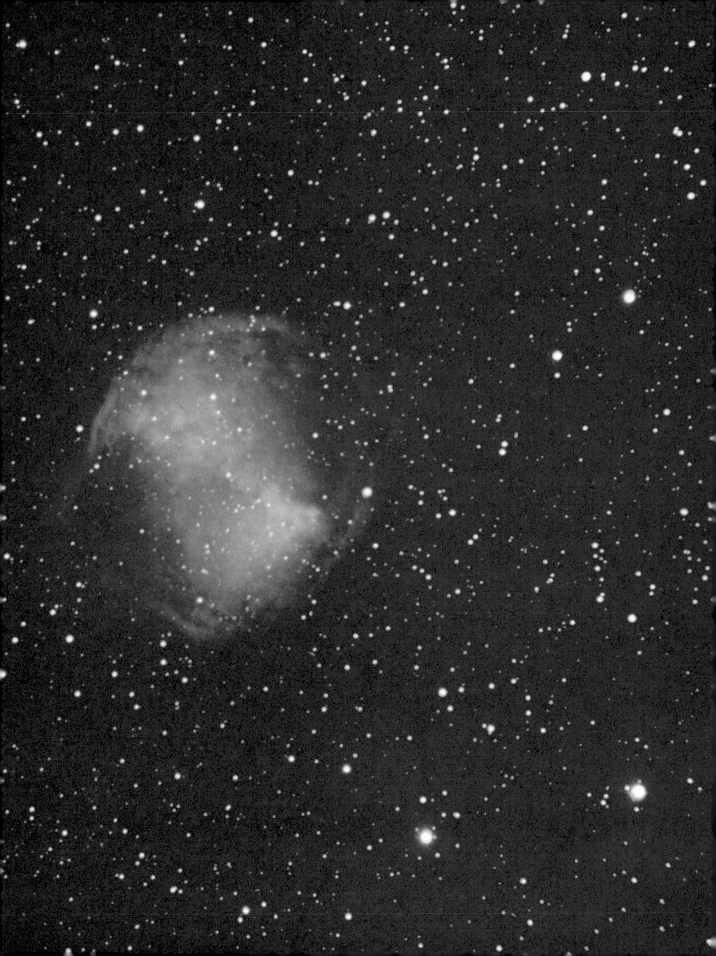

7

The Cosmos beyond the Milky Way

Looking past the nearby stars of the Milky Way, probing the dark distance beyond to discover the shining citadels of other galaxies—this has been the great adventure of 20th Century astronomy.

The sheer size and power of a galaxy can be sensed by anyone on a clear, dark autumn night. Just find a small bright patch in the constellation Andromeda. This is a galaxy so far away—16 quintillion miles—that the light we see left it more than two million years ago. Ancient astronomers noted the Great Nebula in Andromeda, but they did not know the two other galaxies easily seen without a telescope—both in the sky of the Southern Hemisphere. First reported in the 15th Century by Portuguese sailors, they were called the Magellanic Clouds after Magellan, the most famous of these explorers. They are, in a way, our satellite galaxies, held close by the gravitation of the far larger Milky Way.

Through the earliest telescopes astronomers saw many more galaxies, but these still looked so cloudlike that the astronomers could not tell them from actual clouds of dust and gas in the Milky Way. Under

A MYSTERY GALAXY, named NGC 5128 for its listing in the *New General Catalogue*, emits radio noise 1,000 times more intensely than a normal galaxy. Some astronomical observations show that it might be exploding violently. As yet no theory can explain such an intense cosmic event.

the name of "nebulae" (Latin for "clouds"), both distant galaxies and genuine nearby clouds were recorded by early observers mainly because they were nuisances, easy to confuse with approaching comets.

One 18th Century French astronomer, Charles Messier, who hunted comets tirelessly, catalogued 103 nebulae and star clusters—to remind himself to ignore them. As a result, many nearby galaxies are identified today by "Messier," or "M," numbers, honoring a man who hated the sight of them.

When Sir William Herschel compiled the first large catalogue of nebulae, with 2,500 entries, he lumped galaxies and nebulae together. Most of the objects Herschel listed were true nebulae, with only a few galaxies thrown in. So when their spectra were first analyzed in the 1860s, most of them were found to be mere veils of glowing gas. It seemed that the Milky Way was the only true galaxy of stars, and that its extent marked the size of the universe.

But some evidence in favor of other, distant galaxies was beginning to come in. The Earl of Rosse had made out the spiral shape of M 51 in Canes Venatici and had identified 13 other spirals by 1850. The number of spiral-like nebulae continued to grow as the skies were mapped with improving equipment. In 1888, the *New General Catalogue* listed 8,000 nebulae by "NGC" numbers, and well over half of them were spirals. By 1908, when two new *Index Catalogues* of "IC" numbers had been added,

more than 90 per cent of the 13,000 listed nebulae were unrecognized galaxies.

In that same year G. W. Ritchey first photographed individual stars in nearby galaxies. But the first clue to a true measure of the universe was found in 1912. Henrietta S. Leavitt, who was studying Cepheid stars at Harvard Observatory, noticed that the brighter these variable stars are, the more slowly they fluctuate between their bright and their dim periods. The great Danish astronomer, Ejnar Hertzsprung, recognized in Miss Leavitt's discovery a method of measuring the universe. Usually the distance to a star, measured by parallax, is used to change its apparent brightness to its true brightness. Hertzsprung saw that this problem could be turned around because the real brightness of a Cepheid would be known as soon as its pulsation period was observed. Then by comparing its real brightness with its apparent brightness, the Cepheid's distance would be known. This new yardstick would be useful only after the distance of at least one Cepheid was found by a standard method. In 1913 Hertzsprung made the method work, and Cepheids became cosmic beacons that could be used to gauge distances wherever they were visible.

The American astronomer Harlow Shapley was the first to use this new measuring rod. From 1916 to 1918 he studied Cepheids in the clusters of the Milky Way. From his distance measurements of these stars Shap-

Classes of Galaxies

Galaxies have been divided into
four main types. To some
astronomers their shapes and the
kind of stars they contain suggest
that they have taken different
amounts of time to develop.
"Ellipticals," made up largely of
old red stars, may have condensed
from large, dense clouds of star
dust and gas that formed stars
quickly and aged early. "Spirals,"
with their mixture of old and
young stars, may have developed
slowly from lightweight,
disorganized clouds, preserving
part of their star stuff to condense
later. The loosely knit "irregulars"
consist mainly of young blue stars
and large amounts of gas and dust.

ELLIPTICALS

SPIRALS

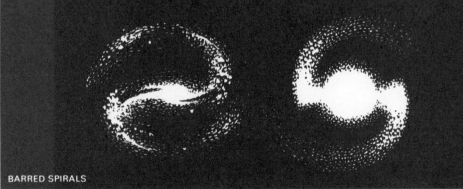

BARRED SPIRALS

IRREGULARS

ley was able to map the Milky Way's halo, then estimate the size of the galaxy and the distance and direction of its hub.

The next major step in the study of galaxies came in 1917 when Ritchey spied a nova in a distant galaxy—NGC 6946, in Cepheus. Most novae reach a true peak brightness over 100,000 times greater than the *true* brightness of the sun. But this one seemed about 2,800 times *fainter* than the faintest star visible without a telescope. To seem so faint, the nova must have blown up several hundred thousand light-years away. Ritchey and other astronomers, notably R. D. Curtis, searched through photographic collections at various observatories and spotted 10 other distant novae that had been overlooked in pictures of nebulae.

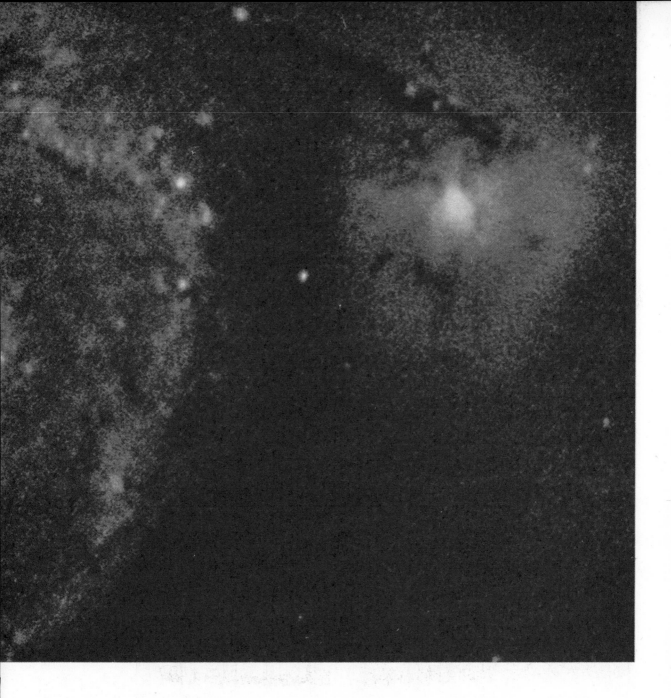

Curtis then announced what seemed to him unquestionable proof that nebulae containing faint novae are really separate galaxies. But conservative astronomers argued that perhaps novae were not all alike in their peak brightness. The wrangle lasted seven years, until Edwin Hubble, using the brand-new 100-inch telescope at Mount Wilson, detected stars in three so-called

A "Whirlpool" in Space

The Whirlpool Galaxy's spiral shape, first detected in 1850 by Lord Rosse, is revealed in detail in this photograph. Swirling around the dense white hub, its star-studded bluish arms glow with supergiants. Its small companion (*right*) is one of the few irregular galaxies with more red than blue stars.

nebulae: M 31 in Andromeda, NGC 6822 and M 33. What was more, some of these stars were Cepheids, and they proved that all three nebulae really were galaxies far beyond the limits of the Milky Way.

Once these distant galaxies had been sighted, Hubble began to study them with Milton Humason, one of the finest technical observers in all astronomy. He soon reached the limits of the Cepheid gauge, a sphere about three million light-years in radius encompassing some 20 galaxies. From there, making rough yardsticks out of brilliant blue supergiants in the arms of galaxies, he went on to chart a farther sphere containing 200 more galaxies, some 30 million light-years in radius.

Still farther out, where single stars were not visible, Hubble gauged distances by the average true brilliance of whole galaxies of the same types as galaxies he had already studied in the 30-million-light-year sphere. With this new measure he raced on out to the then-visible limits of the universe, over a billion light-years away.

Hubble's work was amplified and confirmed by many other observers. Today astronomers know that throughout most of the sky the galaxies they see outnumber single-star images by about six to one. On an average each galaxy contains over a *billion*

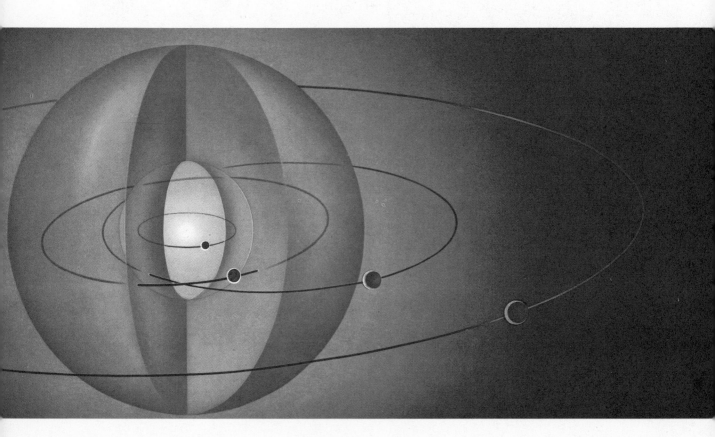

stars—and probably even more planets. From the faintest visible today, the light that reaches the earth has been in transit over five billion years—emitted about the same time that the sun was born.

Galaxies are not all alike. In size most of them are smaller than the Milky Way; a few are larger. In shape they vary from ragged, featureless clouds of brilliance to perfect, star-bejeweled orbs. From earth some appear edge-on, some full face and some tilted in between. Allowing for these different angles, Hubble classified the galaxies by shape in three main families: "spirals," "ellipticals" and "irregulars."

Structurally, the most highly organized

kind of galaxy is a spiral like the Milky Way. It usually has three clearly defined parts: a central hub, a spherical halo of stars and star clusters surrounding the hub and a disk with spiral arms that spin around the hub's equator. Some, called barred spirals, have a cigar-shaped hub that trails spiral arms from each end. Elliptical galaxies consist of just two parts: central hubs and spherical halos. They may be more or less flattened and their hubs may be more or less densely packed with stars, depending on their masses. Irregulars are vaguer still; most of them are chaotic.

Hubble subdivided these families of galaxies into a sequence ranging from the

"Life" on Far-off Planets

Astronomers think that many stars besides the sun have their own planetary systems, and that some of these planets may support some form of life. The drawing at left, of an imaginary star with four planets, shows that only one, the second from its "sun," would remain in the temperature zone (large red sphere) that would permit life. The closest planet would be too hot; the outer two planets would be too cold, even though one swings into the life zone during part of its year. On a planet with low gravity and a thin atmosphere, creatures might be very tall and thin, with huge noses and large lungs to help them breathe more of the thin air (*right*). A water-covered planet might have "people" that resemble fish, while on a planet with very high gravity, the life that evolved might be heavy and sluggish.

LOW-GRAVITY "MAN"

WATER PLANET'S "FISH"

HIGH-GRAVITY "MAN"

115

Do Galaxies Collide?

The two galaxies in this photograph—which broadcast 100 times as much radio energy as a normal galaxy—seem to be colliding. And that is what some astronomers think may be happening. But in effect the two galaxies would pass through each other. Although their gas clouds would buffet each other, causing a great deal of radio energy to be released, the galaxies are so vast, and the stars within them so far apart, that probably not a single pair of stars would actually collide.

calmest and most organized to the most active and least orderly ones. He had set up a framework for all future astronomic studies, but he was aware that larger telescopes might correct his measurements, and he knew that many details of the cosmic picture were still unexplained.

Two of the curious irregularities he had noticed were in M 31, the great galaxy in Andromeda: the individual stars in its hub could not be detected, and its globular clusters seemed to have a true brilliance about four times as faint as the Milky Way's globular clusters. Both facts suggested either that M 31 was basically different from the Milky Way or that it was really several times farther away than the Cepheids in it indicated. Hubble's colleague Walter Baade decided to investigate these puzzles.

Blue-sensitive photographic plates had shown stars in M 31's spiral arms, but with new red-sensitive plates Baade found countless red stars in the hub. "It looked as though the central area and the regions between the arms were populated by one kind of star," he wrote, "whereas another kind predominated in the arms themselves."

Baade's discovery upset so many calculations that it took more than a decade and the power of the new 200-inch Hale telescope to straighten things out. For one thing, the Cepheids in the two populations proved to be different. The ones in the arms were young and bright, while the others were older and dimmer. Shapley had

measured distances by old Cepheids in the Milky Way's halo. But the first ones Hubble found in Andromeda were young, bright ones. Thinking their true brilliance equaled that of the Milky Way Cepheids, he figured the galaxy was much nearer than it is. That was why the globular clusters of M 31 had seemed fainter than those in the Milky Way. They were not really fainter; instead, this galaxy was over twice as far away as anyone had imagined. And so were all the others in which Hubble had used Cepheids to measure distance. Baade had doubled the size of the known universe.

Using the two-population concept, Baade restudied the 20-odd galaxies within three million light-years of the Milky Way, the Local Group that hangs together by gravitation. He saw that elliptical galaxies are made up almost entirely of an ancient halo population, with little dust or gas to form new stars. Spirals such as the Milky Way on the other hand contain both halo and arm populations and varying amounts of free dust and gas. In irregular galaxies, red halo stars are scarce, blue arm stars are plentiful, and potential star stuff sometimes outweighs the lighted stars themselves.

Baade concluded that irregulars probably represent the first stage in the development of galaxies—huge hydrogen clouds full of turbulence as they begin to condense into stars. Some irregular galaxies seem to be developing spiral arms and may eventually evolve into spiral galaxies. Little by little

(Text continued on page 120)

Slow Time at High Speed

Sometime in the far distant future a spaceship may leave the earth, bound for a "nearby" galaxy—perhaps the Andromeda Galaxy, two million light years away. The ship will be far more advanced than any we know today, so advanced, in fact, that it will be able to travel at a speed very close to the speed of light. At such speeds, according to the theory of relativity, time appears to slow down for the ship and its occupants. The trip will require only 28 years, ship's time, to reach Andromeda, and another 28 years to return. An astronaut on board will age 56 years during his journey. But he will not recognize the earth he returns to: the people and places he once knew will be long gone. For during his 56 years in space, his home, the earth, will have become four million years older.

EARTH ON DEPARTURE

118

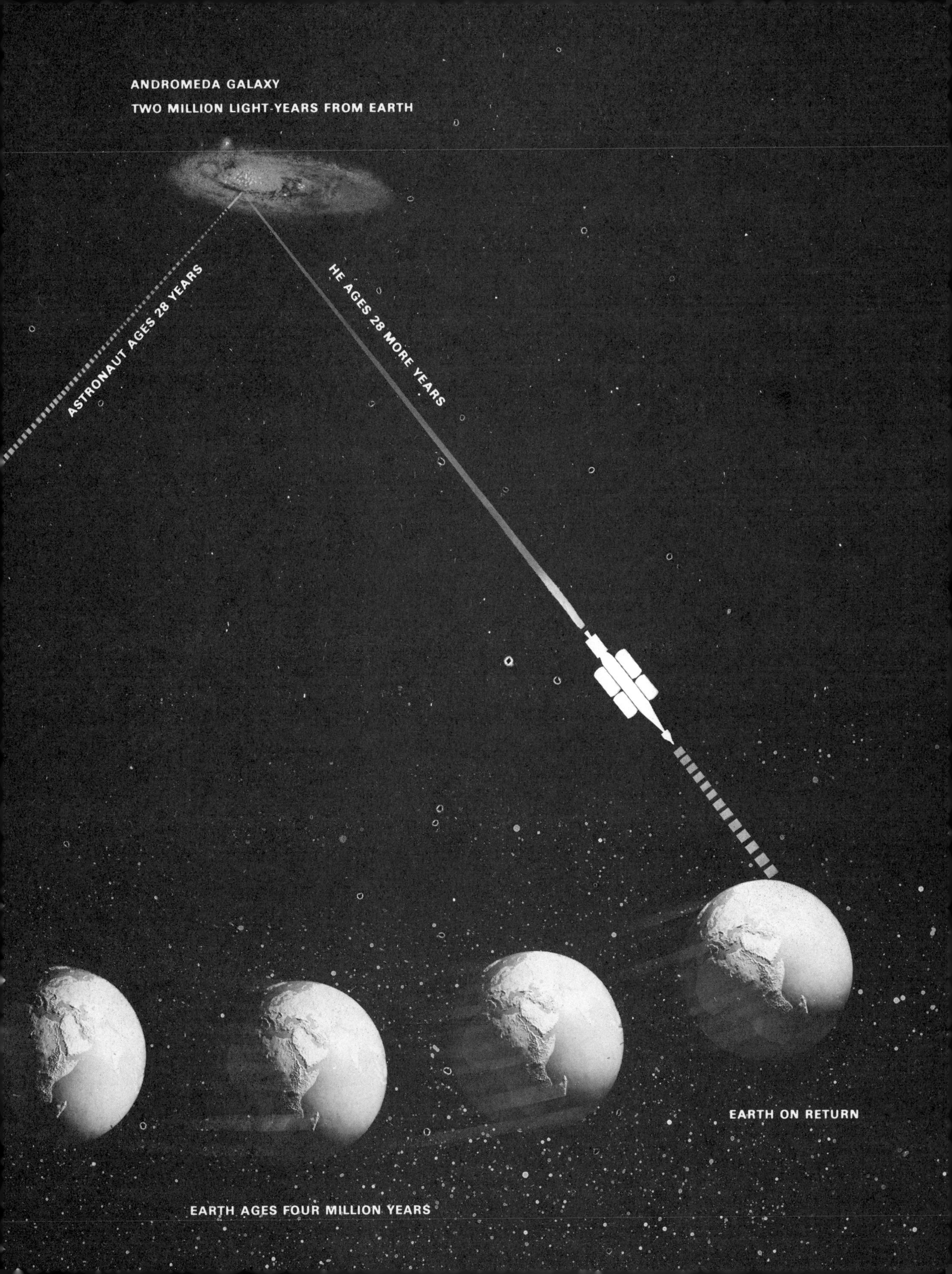

ANDROMEDA GALAXY
TWO MILLION LIGHT-YEARS FROM EARTH

ASTRONAUT AGES 28 YEARS

HE AGES 28 MORE YEARS

EARTH ON RETURN

EARTH AGES FOUR MILLION YEARS

The "Big Bang"

Our universe was born, some scientists believe, in a gigantic cosmic explosion. This idea, called the "big bang" theory, holds that the universe was created some 15 billion years ago, and that all the elements that have ever existed were created in the first half hour of the explosion. Since then, the universe has expanded; the galaxies (*black dots*) have been flying apart—and will continue to do so at ever-increasing speeds, forever.

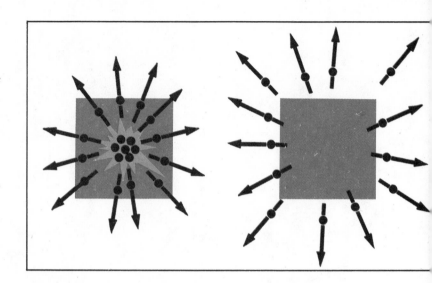

the gassy part of the spiral arms might then be wound inward, tighter and tighter. Stars that had formed out of the gas would be left behind in their orbits, but the free gas that remained would be drawn into the hub and be consumed there. After this the galaxy would become a highly flattened elliptical one. In elliptical galaxies, star formation has apparently ceased. Their clouds of dust and gas have been almost used up.

Besides these various kinds of galaxies, a number of peculiar objects exist in the depths of space: galaxies stretched out of shape or torn apart by forces yet unknown, and many that "shine" for radio telescopes.

No one knows what these "peculiar" galaxies are. Several broadcast so powerfully that a large part of their nuclear energy must be devoted to producing radio waves. One theory suggests that the nuclei of very old or very massive galaxies may eventually explode as the stars in them are crowded closer and closer together. According to this idea, the supernova set off as one star dies touches off a chain reaction among its dying companions, so that the whole nucleus of a galaxy turns into an enormous, slow-burning super-supernova.

Peculiar galaxies have extended astronomers' knowledge of the universe beyond normal visual limits. Most of the peculiars are far more noticeable with radio telescopes than with optical ones. Radio astronomers find their rough bearings and then let Palomar's 200-inch telescope sight in on them. In a similar way, astronomers have discovered puzzling quasi-stellar objects called quasars, which look like stars when photographed with an optical telescope but which emit more energy at radio frequencies than the most powerful known galaxies.

As early as 1912 it was noted that many galaxies and nebulae give off reddened, Doppler-shifted light—as if they must be moving away from the earth. After Hubble

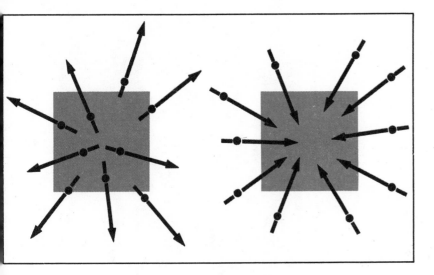

Gravitational Brakes

Scientists who believe in the theory of a "pulsating" universe agree that there was a big bang, and that the universe is expanding. But they think the expansion will slow down and stop, halted by the gravitational pull of all the galaxies on one another. Eventually the galaxies would reverse their direction and come together again at the center of the universe—when another big bang would start the whole process over again.

and Humason began to explore the universe in 1925, they soon found that the "red shift" is a characteristic of all galaxies beyond the small Local Group. The farther they looked out the farther the spectral lines of the galaxies were shifted toward the red end of the spectrum. They concluded that the farther a galaxy is from the Milky Way the faster it is flying away. Only four years after proving that other galaxies exist, Hubble announced that the entire visible universe—hundreds of millions of galaxies—was uniformly expanding in every direction.

Beyond three billion light-years normal galaxies are so faint Doppler shifts can hardly be measured. But one peculiar galaxy, "source 3C 295," has such vast long-wave power that Palomar's Rudolph Minkowski laboriously checked its Doppler shift. The measurement showed that it is rushing away at over a third the speed of light. The rays that man intercepts from it thus would

have been emitted over four billion years ago, and in the meantime it would have traveled much farther away—to about 6.5 billion light-years.

Even beyond this remote galaxy, still farther, fainter objects can be detected. The galaxies barely visible at the limits of the 200-inch telescope are thought to be receding at about two thirds the speed of light; those at the extreme limits of radio telescopes are thought to be escaping at nearly nine tenths the speed of light. Today's distance measurements suggest that the outrushing galaxies have taken about 13 billion years to get where they are.

In expanding, the universe has braked itself as the mutual gravitation of galaxies acted to slow their flights away from each other. The amount of braking that has taken place can be observed in the present, because man, looking out into the universe, is also looking back into the past. Near the limits of vision with Palomar's 200-inch telescope, for instance, galaxies are seen by means of light that left them over five billion light-years away. The amount of Doppler shift in their light shows how fast they were receding then, and the brightness of their light shows how far away they were. In a uniformly expanding universe, galaxies at that distance should move at a certain definite velocity, but the light from the past shows that they were receding faster than that. The extra velocity they once had shows how much gravitation has since braked the expansion of the universe.

The slowdown of distant galaxies supports the theory that our expanding universe will eventually be braked completely and start to shrink again. After billions of years the shrinking universe would reach a superdense, superhot state, and in a gigantic explosion all matter would dissolve again into elemental protons and neutrons. This "big bang" would start the universe expanding again, to repeat its cycle and go on expanding and contracting indefinitely —as in the process matter is neither created nor destroyed but merely rearranged.

Portrait of a Quasar

Quasi-stellar objects, or "quasars," are thought to be among the most distant objects known. Neither stars nor galaxies, they may be as far as ten billion light-years away. This drawing, based on one concept of a quasar, shows exploding stars at the center of a huge cloud of expanding gases.

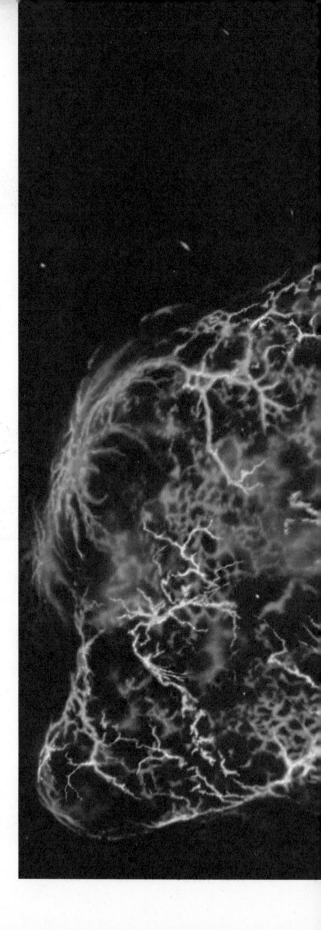

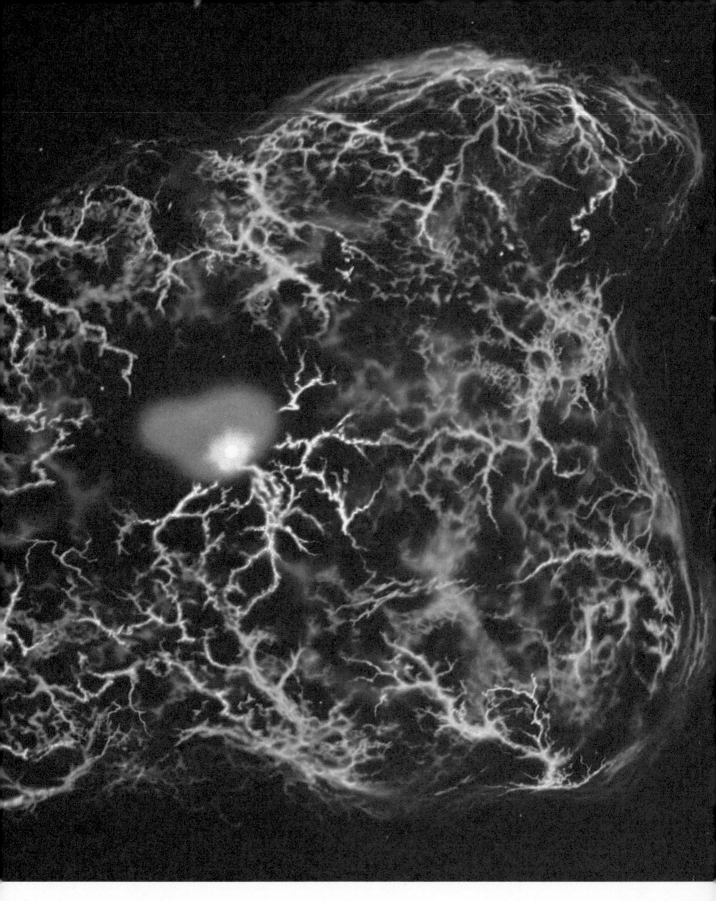

Appendix

GLOSSARY

APHELION: that point of a planet's orbit farthest from the sun.

ASTEROID: a small planetlike body usually orbiting the sun between Mars and Jupiter.

BINARY STARS: two stars revolving closely around each other.

BLUE SHIFT: *see Doppler Effect*.

CEPHEID: *see Pulsating Star*.

CLUSTER:

    GALACTIC: a loose group of stars near the plane of a galaxy.

    GLOBULAR: a compact, spheroidal group of stars in the outskirts of a galaxy.

CONSTELLATION: a group of bright stars making a pattern in the sky; for example, the Little Dipper or Southern Cross.

COPERNICAN SYSTEM: the theory which asserts that the earth rotates on its own axis and revolves around the sun.

DISK STAR: a star located along the plane of the Milky Way or any other spiral galaxy.

DOPPLER EFFECT: the change in wave length observed when a body emitting light is moving toward (blue shift) or away (red shift) from an observer.

ECLIPTIC: the path of the sun across the sky.

    PLANE OF: the plane of the earth's orbit around the sun.

ESCAPE VELOCITY: the speed that an object must attain to overcome the gravitational attraction that holds it to a planet or other celestial body, and escape into space.

GALAXY: a large group of stars isolated in space from other such groups, and often containing quantities of gas and dust.

GIANT: a star 15 to 40 times the diameter of the sun and approximately 100 times more luminous.

HALO: a spherical star cloud surrounding a galaxy.

MAIN-SEQUENCE STAR: one of a class of stars that show an orderly relationship between brightness, size and temperature.

MESSIER (M) NUMBER: the designation of nebulae and star clusters in the Messier catalogue.

MILKY WAY: the local galaxy, of which the sun is a member. Saucer-shaped, it looks like a river of stars in the sky because it is seen edge on from the earth.

NEBULA: a hazy cloud of dust and gas outside the solar system. The term was formerly applied also to galaxies.

NGC NUMBER: the designation of nebulae and star clusters in the *New General Catalogue*.

NOVA: a star that becomes unstable, suddenly flaring up and then subsiding.

PERIHELION: that point on a planet's orbit closest to the sun.

PTOLEMAIC SYSTEM: a theory dominant until the 16th Century, asserting that the sun, moon, planets and stars all revolved around the earth.

PULSATING STAR: one that periodically expands and then contracts. Includes such stars as the Cepheids and RR Lyrae types used to measure celestial distance.

RED SHIFT: *see Doppler Effect*.

SOLAR SYSTEM: the sun and its planets, satellites, asteroids and comets.

SPECTRAL CLASS: the classification of stars according to the principal features in their spectra.

SUPERGIANT: a star approximately 50,000 times more brilliant than the sun and billions of miles in diameter.

SUPERNOVA: a very unstable star that suddenly explodes catastrophically.

TRANSIT: the passage of a small celestial body across the face of a larger one.

VARIABLE STAR: one whose brightness varies periodically for reasons other than "twinkling" due to the earth's atmosphere.

WHITE DWARF: a planet-sized star with great density.

ZODIAC: a band of constellations around the heavens centered on the ecliptic.

THE BRIGHTEST STARS WE SEE

NAME OF STAR	TRUE BRIGHTNESS (SUN EQUALS 1)	DISTANCE AWAY (LIGHT-YEARS)
Alpha Canis Majoris (Sirius)	23	8.7
Alpha Carinae (Canopus)	1,500	98
Alpha Centauri	1.5	4.3
Alpha Boötis (Arcturus)	116	36
Alpha Lyrae (Vega)	55	27
Alpha Aurigae (Capella)	150	45
Beta Orionis (Rigel)	60,000	900
Alpha Canis Minoris (Procyon)	7.2	11.3
Alpha Orionis (Betelgeuse)	15,000	520
Alpha Eridani (Achernar)	718	118
Beta Centauri	10,400	490
Alpha Aquilae (Altair)	11.4	165
Alpha Crucis	5,000	370
Alpha Tauri (Aldebaran)	164	68
Alpha Virginis (Spica)	1,800	220
Alpha Scorpii (Antares)	9,500	520
Beta Geminorum (Pollux)	34	35
Alpha Piscis Austrini (Fomalhaut)	13.7	23
Alpha Cygni (Deneb)	60,000	1,600
Beta Crucis	6,000	490
Alpha Leonis (Regulus)	164	84
Epsilon Canis Majoris (Adhara)	9,500	680
Lambda Scorpii (Shaula)	1,800	710
Alpha Geminorum (Castor)	36	45
Gamma Orionis (Bellatrix)	4,000	470

THE BEST-KNOWN COMETS

COMET	PERIOD IN YEARS	DATE FIRST OBSERVED	NEXT DUE
Encke	3.30	1786	1981
Honda-Mrkos-Pajdusakova	5.22	1948	1980
Tuttle-Giacobini-Kresak	5.49	1858	1978
Giacobini-Zinner	6.41	1900	1979
Pons-Winnecke	6.34	1819	1983
Perrine Mrkos	6.72	1896	1982
Schwassmann-Wachmann II	6.54	1929	1981
d'Arrest	6.23	1851	1982
Brooks II	6.72	1889	1980
Finlay	6.90	1886	1981
Borrelly	6.99	1905	1981
Faye	7.41	1843	1979
Whipple	7.47	1933	1985
Wolf I	8.43	1884	1984
Comas Sola	8.55	1927	1978
Tuttle I	13.80	1790	1981
Neujmin I	17.90	1913	1984
Westphal	61.90	1852	2037
Pons-Brooks	71.00	1812	2025
Halley	76.10	240 B.C.	1986

THE SOLAR SYSTEM

BODY	MILLION MILES FROM SUN	AVERAGE DIAMETER IN MILES	"YEAR"	"DAY"	KNOWN SATELLITES	ESCAPE VELOCITY MILES/SEC.	MASS (BILLION BILLION TONS)
Mercury	36	2,910	88 days	180 days	none	2.6	360
Venus	67	7,580	225 days	243 days	none	6.4	5,360
Earth	93	7,910	1 year	1 day	1	6.9	6,590
Mars	142	4,140	1.9 years	24.6 hours	2	3.1	705
Jupiter	483	86,600	11.9 years	10 hours	12	35.7	2,090,000
Saturn	888	72,300	29.7 years	10.5 hours	10	22.0	625,000
Uranus	1,780	29,500	83.7 years	10.7 hours	5	13.6	96,000
Neptune	2,800	27,800	166 years	12.7 hours	2	15.1	116,000
Pluto	3,660	3,700	247.7 years	6.4 days	none	unknown	unknown
Sun	———	864,000	———	25-33 days	———	383.0	2,200,000,000
Moon	———	2,160	———	27.3 days	———	1.5	81

Index

Numerals in italics indicate a photograph or painting of the subject listed.

Credits

The sources for the illustrations in this book are shown below. Credits for the pictures from left to right are separated by commas, from top to bottom by dashes.

Cover—William C. Miller, Mount Wilson and Palomar Observatories

Table of Contents—Simone D. Gossner—Jean Held—Otto van Eersel—Gaetano Di Palma—Frank Vincent Vitullo—Jean Held—Frank Vincent Vitullo

6-7—Simone D. Gossner

9—Smithsonian Institution, Simone D. Gossner

10—Simone D. Gossner, Smithsonian Institution

13—Simone D. Gossner, N. R. Farbman /University of California

14—Eric Schaal /Metropolitan Museum of Art

15—Smithsonian Institution, Eric Schaal /Metropolitan Museum of Art

16 to 19—Matt Greene

21—Antonio Petruccelli

22-23—U.S. Navy

25—Matt Greene

26—Frank Vincent Vitullo

28—Jim Egleson

29—Walter Sanders /Museo di Storia della Scienza, Florence, Simone D. Gossner

30-31—Jim Egleson

32-33—Max Gschwind

34—Mt. Wilson and Palomar Observatories, Jim Egleson

35—J. R. Eyerman

36-37—Ralph Crane, Jim Egleson

38-39—(top) Jean Held—Tom Hutchins, Max Gschwind, Gordon Tenney, Ken Kay

40-41—Otto van Eersel /The Crowell-Collier Publishing Co., Harland Nasvik

42-43—Fritz Goro

44—Russ Kinne from Photo Researchers

47—Mel Hunter (symbols Matt Greene)

49—E. C. Slipher, Lowell Observatory

50-51—NASA, UPI photo from NASA

52-53—W. S. Finsen of Union Observatory, Johannesburg —Matt Greene

54-55—Otto van Eersel

56-57—California Institute of Technology and Carnegie Institution of Washington, Otto van Eersel

58-59—Dr. Robert C. Leighton, Chesley Bonestell

60—Mel Hunter

62-63—Nino Carbe, Gaetano Di Palma

64-65—C. O. Lampland and E. C. Slipher, Lowell Observatory

66—Official U.S. Navy photo, Canton Island Expedition, 1937

68-69—Ray Manley from Shostal, Jim Egleson

70—J. R. Eyerman

72-73—Mark A. Binn

74-75—Antonio Petruccelli

76-77—High Altitude Observatory, Boulder, Colo.

78-79—Gaetano Di Palma, Mt. Wilson and Palomar Observatories

80-81—Matt Greene

82-83—Mel Hunter

84-85—Mt. Wilson and Palomar Observatories photo by William C. Miller; © 1959 California Institute of Technology

86—Arthur D. Code and Theodore E. Houck of the University of Wisconsin— Max Gschwind for FORTUNE

88-89—Frank Vincent Vitullo, George V. Kelvin

92—Mt. Wilson and Palomar Observatories

94-95—Mt. Wilson and Palomar Observatories photo by William C. Miller; © 1959 California Institute of Technology

96—Ralph Crane from Black Star

98—U.S. Air Force

101—Jean Held

102-103—Mt. Wilson and Palomar Observatories photo by William C. Miller; © 1959 California Institute of Technology, Official U.S. Navy Photo by Arthur A. Hoag

104—Mt. Wilson and Palomar Observatories photo by William C. Miller; © 1959 California Institute of Technology

105—Mt. Wilson and Palomar Observatories

106-107—Mt. Wilson and Palomar Observatories photo by William C. Miller; © 1959 California Institute of Technology

108—Mt. Wilson and Palomar Observatories

111—Nino Carbe

112-113—Official U.S. Navy photo by Arthur A. Hoag

114—Max Gschwind for FORTUNE

115—Anthony Saris from a drawing by Fred Freeman

116—Mt. Wilson and Palomar Observatories

118-119—Geo-Physical Globe by Rand-McNally and Co. and Arthur Lidov

120-121—Frank Vincent Vitullo

122-123—George V. Kelvin

End papers—Dirk Laninga

For Further Reading

Angrist, Stanley W.: *How Our World Came to Be.* Crowell, 1969. *Other Worlds, Other Beings.* Crowell, 1973.

Asimov, Isaac, *Jupiter, the Largest Planet.* Lothrop, Lee & Sheppard, 1976.

Beiser, Germaine, *The Story of the Earth's Magnetic Field.* Dutton, 1964.

Bendick, Jeanne, *The First Book of Time.* Franklin Watts, 1963.

Branley, Franklyn M., *Mars: Planet Number Four* (rev. ed.). Crowell, 1966.

Chamberlain, Joseph Miles, *Planets, Stars and Space.* Creative Educational Society, 1962.

Chester, Michael and Allert, *Let's Go on a Space Shuttle.* G. P. Putnam's Sons, 1976.

Clark, Mary Lou, *You and Relativity.* Children's Press, 1965.

Drake, Frank D., *Intelligent Life in Space.* Macmillan, 1962.

Engdahl, Sylvia L., *The Planet-Girded Suns.* Atheneum, 1974.

Gallant, Roy A., *Exploring the Moon.* Doubleday, 1966.

Haber, Heinz, *Stars, Man and Atoms.* Golden Press, 1962.

Heintze, Carl, *Search Among the Stars.* Van Nostrand, 1966.

Kraske, Robert, *Is There Life in Outer Space?* Harcourt Brace Jovanovich, 1976.

Mayall, Newton, *The Sky Observer's Guide.* Golden Press, 1961.

Nourse, Alan, *The Giant Planets.* Franklin Watts, 1974.

Reed, W. Maxwell, *The Stars for Sam* (rev. ed.). Harcourt, Brace and World, 1960.

Simon, Tony, *The Search for Planet X.* Basic Books, 1962.

Wyler, Rose, *The New Golden Book of Astronomy* (rev. ed.). Golden Press, 1965.

Zim, Herbert S., *The Universe.* William Morrow, 1973.

Acknowledgments

The editors of this book are indebted to Kenneth L. Franklin, American Museum—Hayden Planetarium, New York City, who read and commented on the text. The editors are also indebted to the staff of the original LIFE Nature Library edition of *The Universe*, from which this volume has been adapted. The staff for this volume was Ogden Tanner, editor; Eric Gluckman, designer; Jonathan Kastner, writer; Eleanor Feltser, Susan Marcus, Paula Norworth, Theo Pascal, researchers; Grace Fitzgerald, copyreader; Gloria Cernosia, art assistant.